D1268078
CITY OF HOUSTON TEXAS
GIFT
Houston Endowment, Inc.

Transactions (TRUDY) of the Geophysics Institute
of the Academy of Sciences of the USSR, No. 39 (166)

МИКРОСТРУКТУРА И МАКРОСТРУКТУРА УПРУГИХ ВОЛН

В ОДНОМЕРНЫХ НЕПРЕРЫВНЫХ НЕОДНОРОДНЫХ СРЕДАХ

THE MICROSTRUCTURE AND MACROSTRUCTURE OF ELASTIC WAVES

IN ONE-DIMENSIONAL CONTINUOUS NONHOMOGENEOUS MEDIA

SOVIET RESEARCH IN GEOPHYSICS
In English Translation
Volume 3

Acad. of Sciences of the U.S.S.R.
+ Geophysics Inst.

THE MICROSTRUCTURE AND MACROSTRUCTURE OF ELASTIC WAVES

IN ONE-DIMENSIONAL CONTINUOUS NONHOMOGENEOUS MEDIA

B. N. Ivakin

AMERICAN GEOPHYSICAL UNION
Consultants Bureau, New York

Originally published by the Geophysics Institute of the Academy of Sciences of the USSR as Trudy Geofizicheskogo Instituta No. 39 (166) under the title "Mikrostruktura i makrostruktura uprugikh voln b odnomernykh nepreryvnykh neodnorodnykh sredakh" in Moscow in 1958.

Library of Congress Card Number 60-9253

1515 Massachusetts Ave., N. W.
Washington 5, D. C.

TRANSLATED AND PRODUCED BY CONSULTANTS BUREAU ENTERPRISES, INC.

Printed and Bound in the U. S. A.

61-39368

CONTENTS

	Page
Foreword	vii
Introduction	1
Section 1. Determination of the Integral and Differential Propagation Constants of a Nonhomogeneous Waveguide, and the Relationship between Them	4
Section 2. Determination of the Input Impedances of a Nonhomogeneous Waveguide	19
Section 3. Incidence of a Plane Wave Normal to the Interface Separating Two Elastic Half-Spaces	26
Section 4. Incidence of a Plane Wave Normal to a Layer Located between Two Elastic Half-Spaces	45
Section 5. Incidence of a Plane Wave Normal to the Layers of a Periodically Layered Elastic Medium	63
Conclusions	107
Summary	109
Literature Cited	111

FOREWORD

This issue discusses problems of the structure of waves propagating in continuous nonhomogeneous and generally absorbing media, with a single spatial coordinate, over intervals infinitesimally small or comparable with a wavelength (microstructure of the waves) and over intervals larger or appreciably larger than a wavelength (macrostructure of the waves).

Solutions are obtained for wave problems, in operator form, for absorbing media: 1) with a single interface, 2) with two interfaces, and 3) with periodically repeating layers.

In the cases considered, the micro- and macrostructure of sinusoidal waves of displacement, pressure, and intensity are studied in detail. The possibilities of obtaining solutions to the wave problems in media having smoothly varying parameters are considered.

In this book the Russian abbreviations for the trignometric functions have been used. These differ slightly from the abbreviations commonly used in the United States, for example:

sin	sin
cos	cos
tan	tg
cot	ctn
sinh	sh
cosh	ch
tanh	th
coth	cth
arc sin	arcsin
arc tan	arctg
arc sinh	Arsh
arc coth	Arch
arc tanh	Arth

INTRODUCTION

In up-to-date correlation seismic techniques for exploration of useful minerals, seismographs are set up, as a rule, at distances smaller than a wavelength. Travel-time and amplitude curves on baselines smaller than a wavelength are frequently complicated by a number of details associated with the microstructure of waves in a nonhomogeneous medium. The microstructure of the waves in nonhomogeneous media is construed to embrace the wave characteristics (velocity of propagation, amplitude variations) determined on baselines infinitesimally small or comparable with the wavelength in the medium.

Accordingly, the macrostructure of waves in a nonhomogeneous medium is construed to embrace wave characteristics measured on baselines larger or appreciably larger than the wavelength in the medium in question.

The microstructure of elastic waves in one-dimensional nonhomogeneous media has not been treated in the literature on the basis of exact dynamical representations, as far as the author is aware. However, those questions, aside from their general physical interest, are also of interest in seismic prospecting, and in particular with reference to such problems as seismic logging of a layered medium, or observations at the surface under conditions of vertically layered media, etc.

The problems considered below with reference to the micro- and macrostructure of waves in nonhomogeneous media are acknowledged to indicate the limits of applicability of the principles of geometric seismics, and also serve to facilitate the study of the complete wave pattern in the simplest one-dimensional[1] media: 1) with a single interface, 2) with two interfaces and, 3) with periodically repeating layers.

For the study of the wave problems referred to, use is made of the extensively developed computational device of the theory of four-pole networks and transmission lines, the basis of which has been outlined in detail in a number of papers [1, 2, 3, 4]. In order to make use of the computational equipment in the theory referred to, we consider a three-dimensional continuous medium consisting, in the general case, of an arbitrary number of plane-parallel layers – a mechanical transmission line – arbitrarily placed normally to the layers of the medium. In this and in all of the subsequent cases, it is assumed that a plane wave propagates through the medium in a direction normal to the layers comprising the medium.

The nonhomogeneous mechanical transmission line so obtained (an acoustical waveguide) may be reduced to its electric analog, a nonuniform electrical transmission line. However, by virtue of the well developed theory of electromechanical analogs [5, 6, 7], we shall not need to resort to electrical analogs, particularly in view of the fact that a computational representation [1], translated from the field of electric circuits and transmission lines, is already available for application to mechanical systems and transmission lines.

In the theory of four-pole networks, widespread use is made of the abstract concept of the replacement of a nonuniform transmission line, consisting of continuous uniform sections, by its equivalent four-pole network consisting of lumped impedances (arms). The equivalent four-pole network with its impedance arms chosen in a certain way in relation to the external work (of oscillatory modes at its terminals) duplicates fully, for all frequencies, the external work of the substituted nonuniform line. This substitution often proves convenient for the purpose of computing the external work done by a nonuniform line (nonhomogeneous waveguide).

[1] The one-dimensional media considered here include both one-dimensional media and two- and three-dimensional plane-parallel layered media equivalent to one-dimensional media in the familiar sense, where one of the coordinates, x for instance, along which a plane wave propagates, is perpendicular to the successive layers.

Thus, the theory of four-pole networks and transmission lines is designed to determine the external (integral) wave characteristics of nonuniform transmission lines, without establishing their internal wave properties. In view of that fact, the author introduces the concept of the propagation constant of a nonhomogeneous waveguide over an infinitesimally small baseline [8] (known in what follows as the differential propagation constant), assuming its parameters to be known. The latter concept makes it possible to determine the internal wave characteristics of the waveguide over infinitesimally small baselines and to study accordingly the microstructure of the propagating wave. In addition, with the aid of the differential propagation constant, it is a comparatively simple matter to pose the problem arising in one-dimensional media with smoothly varying elastic characteristics, leading to a conventional differential equation of the first order.

The solutions of the wave problems posed are presented in operator notation, making it possible to study nonsteady-state oscillations, although detailed calculations and graphs are given for steady-state sinusoidal oscillations.

SECTION ONE

DETERMINATION OF THE INTEGRAL AND DIFFERENTIAL PROPAGATION CONSTANTS OF A NONHOMOGENEOUS WAVEGUIDE, AND THE RELATIONSHIP BETWEEN THEM

An elastic wave (cf. [9, 10, 11, 12, 13]) propagating without losses along a uniform infinite waveguide (a mechanical transmission line) comprises, at any point along the waveguide, an in-phase set of pressure waves $\bar{T}$ and of velocity waves $\bar{V}$, as well as an intensity wave $\bar{Q} = \bar{V} \cdot \bar{T}$. The input impedance of that type of guide does not vary from point to point, and is equal to the wave impedance $\overline{W}$ which, as we know, is defined at any point along the guide by the ratio of pressure to velocity $\overline{W} = \frac{\overline{T}}{\overline{V}}$. The phase velocity of all modes, determined over any interval and at any point of the waveguide in question, is a constant magnitude and depends solely on the elastic characteristics of the medium $c = \sqrt{\frac{K_0}{M_0}}$, where K_0 is the modulus of rigidity of the waveguide, and M_0 is the density of the waveguide. This type of wave will be known as homogeneous. In the case of steady state oscillations (e.g., of a wave impulse) in a homogeneous waveguide without dispersion or attenuation, the elastic wave will also be homogeneous.

Wave processes occurring in a nonhomogeneous waveguide become highly complex. Elastic waves at the interfaces of such a waveguide are subject to reflections; waves of different modes (pressure, velocity, and intensity waves) are reflected from the same interface in obedience to different laws. In a waveguide having smoothly varying parameters or consisting of a large number of different homogeneous sections, complex interference phenomena take place[1], often giving rise to appreciable shifts of the pressure wave with respect to the velocity wave. As a result, the wave impedance $\overline{W}=\frac{\overline{T}}{\overline{V}}$ becomes a complex quantity (an imaginary component arises), and at those points where the shift in the pressure wave with respect to the velocity wave reaches a quarter wavelength $\left(\frac{\pi}{2}\right)$, the wave impedance becomes purely imaginary, as for example in standing waves.

The phase velocity of waves, determined over an infinitesimally small interval of a nonhomogeneous waveguide, varies from point to point, presenting higher or lower values compared to those obtained from the elastic characteristics (parameters) of that waveguide section, $c=\sqrt{\frac{K_0}{M_0}}$. Accordingly, determination of the phase velocity based solely on elastic characteristics yields erroneous results.

The wave properties of a nonhomogeneous waveguide will be substantially different in the case of transient and in the case of steady-state oscillations. In the latter case, the wave properties of waveguides have some asymptotic state to which the wave properties of a waveguide fed by an abruptly connected source with a periodic (e.g., sinusoidal) form of oscillations[2] tends. An elastic wave traveling down a nonhomogeneous guide will "decay" at the interfaces into two fundamental trains of waves advancing in two opposite directions. There will be a relation between those trains of waves: the train going in one direction is replenished ("fed") at the inter-

---

[1] For a treatment of interference phenomena on a plane and in space, investigated for purposes of seismic explorations, see the thesis of I. P. Kosminskii [14].

[2] Note that in the case of a periodically nonhomogeneous waveguide (two, three or more homogeneous sections of the waveguide repeat periodically), where the period λ_n of the nonhomogeneity of the waveguide is much less than the dominant wavelength of the wave impulse λ_p, the difference between the transient and nonsteady modes of oscillation becomes insignificant, and in the limit where $\lambda_n \to 0$, and λ_p is finite, we have in essence a homogeneous waveguide and, as a consequence, a homogeneous transmission line.

faces by the energy associated with the second train of waves advancing in the opposite direction, and vice versa. In addition, this relationship is manifested over the homogeneous intervals of the waveguide as well, which leads, for example, to a variation in the phase velocity from one point to another of the guide, reference to which was made above.

In the case of transient oscillations, replenishment of the energy of one series of waves at the expense of the other takes place not constantly, but in batch transfers of energy. In the case of steady-state oscillations, we have a sort of equilibrium state which is characterized by a constant energy exchange between the trains of waves proceeding in different directions.

Suppose that we could deflect the series of waves going in the opposite direction "off to the side," to remove it from consideration; then we would be dealing with homogeneous waves going in only one direction, the forward direction, over the homogeneous sections of a nonhomogeneous waveguide. In addition, if we were capable of taking into account all of those additional sources of wave energy which exist at the interfaces as a result of the reflecting properties of the latter, and add to the energy of the forward-going train of waves, then we would again be dealing with homogeneous waves in the homogeneous sections of the guide. Then, in the case of steady-state oscillations, a phase lag or lead of the total wave would appear at the interfaces, relative to the state of things in the waveguide before the additional energy sources at the interfaces were taken into account. In the case of transient oscillations, as a result of the effect of the additional sources at the interfaces, we would have a distortion of the shape of the homogeneous wave in the guide.

Now, in discussing the wave properties of a nonhomogeneous waveguide, we must investigate the entire set of waves excited by a single source in the waveguide. That set of waves is known, in a nonhomogeneous waveguide, as the resultant wave.

Resultant waves in nonhomogeneous waveguides, with known laws governing the variation of the parameters, may be described and studied with the aid of input impedances playing the role of wave impedances, and of propagation constants for the corresponding modes.

Integral Propagation Constants $\vec{S}$[1]

The study of the general (external) wave properties of a nonhomogeneous waveguide coincident with the x axis will be carried out with the aid of the integral propagation constant $\vec{S}$. The latter is determined in the following manner.

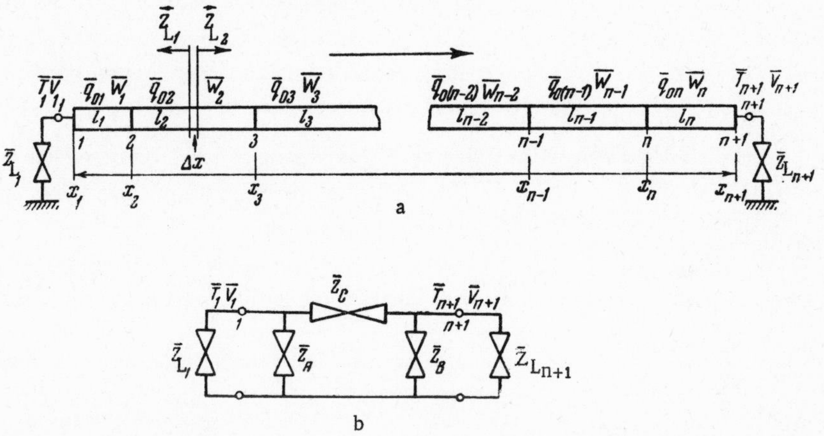

Fig. 1. A nonhomogeneous acoustical waveguide (mechanical transmission line) (a), and its representation by an equivalent mechanical four-pole network (b), with all external wave properties of the guide retained.

Suppose that we have given a nonhomogeneous waveguide (Fig. 1a) consisting of n homogeneous sections, with a known law governing the distribution of parameters $\bar{q}_0$; $\bar{W}$; l: 1) $\bar{q}_{01}$; $\bar{W}_1$; l_1; 2) $\bar{q}_{02}$; $\bar{W}_2$; l_2; 3) $\bar{q}_{03}$; $\bar{W}_3$; l_3...; $n-1$) $\bar{q}_{0\,(n-1)}$; $\bar{W}_{n-1}$; l_{n-1}; n) $\bar{q}_{0n}$; $\bar{W}_n$; l_n where $\bar{q}_0$ is the propagation constant of the respective homogeneous section of the waveguide, referred to unit wavelength; $\bar{W}$ is the wave impedance of the corresponding homogeneous section of the waveguide; l is the length of the homogeneous section; $\bar{Z}_{L_1}$, $\bar{Z}_{L\,n+1}$ are the load mechanical impedances of the nonhomogeneous waveguide.

The sections of the nonhomogeneous waveguide may possess discrete parameters (as for example an artificial mechanical transmission line), different types of resistive losses, etc., which in the

---

[1] Here, and in what follows, the arrow pointing to the right over a letter denotes the forward direction of propagation of the wave under study, and the arrow pointing to the left indicates backward propagation

last analysis have an effect on the values of $\bar{q}_0$ and $\bar{W}$, which are in the general case functions of the Heaviside operator p.

The integral propagation constant is determined for the entire nonhomogeneous waveguide taken as a unit:

$$\vec{S}_T = \ln \frac{\bar{T}}{\bar{T}_n}; \quad \vec{S}_V = \ln \frac{\bar{V}_1}{\bar{V}_n}, \tag{1a}$$

where $\vec{S}_T$ is the integral propagation constant of the pressure wave, $\vec{S}_V$ the integral propagation constant of a velocity wave.

The transmission constant of a nonhomogeneous waveguide, according to [2], is equal to the half sum of the integral propagation constants of the pressure and velocity waves

$$\vec{\theta}_S = \frac{1}{2}(\vec{S}_T + \vec{S}_V) = \vec{S}_Q. \tag{1b}$$

The transmission constant will be denoted in what follows, for purposes of generality, as the propagation constant of an intensity wave, and will be designated as $\vec{S}_Q$.

The integral propagation constants $\vec{S}_T$ and $\vec{S}_V$, according to their definition, express the wave properties of the waveguide separately for pressure waves and for velocity waves. For steady-state sinusoidal oscillations, they determine the following:

$$\vec{S}_T = \alpha_T + i\beta_T; \quad \vec{S}_V = \alpha_V + i\beta_V, \tag{2}$$

where $i = \sqrt{-1}$; α_T and α_V are the damping coefficients, respectively, of the pressure wave and velocity wave; β_T and β_V are the phase constants, respectively, of the pressure wave and velocity wave, in terms of which the phase velocities of the corresponding modes in a nonhomogeneous waveguide taken as a whole may be defined.

The integral propagation constants, as will be apparent from the subsequent discussion, are functions of the propagation constants $\bar{q}_0$, the wave impedances $\bar{W}$ of homogeneous sections of the guide, of the length l and the load $\bar{Z}_L$ of each end of the waveguide toward which the wave under study is moving, i.e.

$$\left.\begin{aligned} \vec{S}_T &= f_T(\bar{q}_{01}; \bar{q}_{02}; \bar{q}_{03} \ldots \bar{q}_{0n}; \bar{W}_1; \bar{W}_2; \bar{W}_3 \ldots \bar{W}_n; l_1; l_2; l_3 \ldots l_n; \bar{Z}_{L n+1}), \\ \vec{S}_V &= f_V(\bar{q}_{01}; \bar{q}_{02}; \bar{q}_{03} \ldots \bar{q}_{0n}; \bar{W}_1; \bar{W}_2; \bar{W}_3 \ldots \bar{W}_n; l_1; l_2; l_3 \ldots l_n; \bar{Z}_{L n+1}). \end{aligned}\right\} \tag{3}$$

As we know from the theory of four-pole networks [1, 2, 4] [1], any nonhomogeneous waveguide (mechanical transmission line) may be represented by its equivalent unbalanced four-pole network with the external wave properties of the nonhomogeneous waveguide fully retained. Consider a nonhomogeneous waveguide (Fig. 1a) represented by a pi-type mechanical section (Fig. 1b). In order for the external wave properties of the nonhomogeneous waveguide to be fully retained, we shall require a certain relationship to prevail between the mechanical impedances of the pi-section, i.e., the mechanical impedances $\bar{Z}_A$, $\bar{Z}_B$, $\bar{Z}_C$, of the network arms, on the values of $\bar{q}_0$, $\bar{W}$ and l for the nonhomogeneous waveguide. In the general case, we have:

$$\left.\begin{aligned} \bar{Z}_A &= F_A(\bar{q}_{01};\ \bar{q}_{02}\ldots\bar{q}_{0n};\ \bar{W}_1;\ \bar{W}_2\ldots\bar{W}_n;\ l_1;\ l_2\ldots l_n); \\ \bar{Z}_B &= F_B(\bar{q}_{01};\ \bar{q}_{02}\ldots\bar{q}_{0n};\ \bar{W}_1;\ \bar{W}_2\ldots\bar{W}_n;\ l_1;\ l_2\ldots l_n); \\ \bar{Z}_C &= F_C(\bar{q}_{01};\ \bar{q}_{02}\ldots\bar{q}_{0n};\ \bar{W}_1;\ \bar{W}_2\ldots\bar{W}_n;\ l_1;\ l_2\ldots l_n). \end{aligned}\right\} \quad (4)$$

Then the propagation constants $\vec{S}_T$ and $\vec{S}_V$ may be expressed in the following manner in terms of the impedances of the equivalent four-pole network:

$$\begin{aligned} \vec{S}_T &= F_T(\bar{Z}_A;\ \bar{Z}_B;\ \bar{Z}_C;\ \bar{Z}_{L_n+1}), \\ \vec{S}_V &= F_V(\bar{Z}_A;\ \bar{Z}_B;\ \bar{Z}_C;\ \bar{Z}_{L_n+1}), \end{aligned} \quad (5)$$

or

$$\begin{aligned} \vec{S}_T &= F_T(F_A;\ F_B;\ F_C;\ Z_{L_n+1}), \\ \vec{S}_V &= F_V(F_A;\ F_B;\ F_C;\ Z_{L_n+1}). \end{aligned} \quad (6)$$

We then assign the condition $f_T = F_T$; $f_V = F_V$, , which assures the identity of the wave properties of the nonhomogeneous waveguide and those of the equivalent four-pole network.

$\overleftarrow{S}_T$ and $\overleftarrow{S}_V$ for the reverse direction of travel of the wave may be defined in similar fashion.

The theory of four-pole networks tells us [4] that a nonhomogeneous waveguide and the equivalent quadripole (Fig. 1) retain their equivalence for all frequencies when loaded by any other, but identical, impedances $\bar{Z}'_{L_1}$ and $\bar{Z}'_{L_n}$. They also retain their equiv-

---

[1] Literature references are given not only for mechanical four-pole networks, but also for electrical quadripoles, assuming the transition from one to the other to be known from a study of the techniques of the theory of electromechanical analogies.

alence when loaded with a zero or infinite mechanical impedance. This provides the possibility of expressing the impedances of the arms of an equivalent four-pole network (section) $\bar{Z}_A$, $\bar{Z}_B$, $\bar{Z}_C$, in terms of the input impedances of a short-circuited $(Z_L=0)$ and open-circuited $(Z_L=\infty)$ quadripole:

$$\left.\begin{aligned}\bar{Z}_C&=\sqrt{\bar{Z}_{\infty n}(\bar{Z}_{\infty 1}-\bar{Z}_{01})}=\sqrt{\bar{Z}_{\infty 1}(\bar{Z}_{\infty n}-\bar{Z}_{0n})}\,;\\ \bar{Z}_A&=\bar{Z}_{\infty 1}-\sqrt{\bar{Z}_{\infty n}(\bar{Z}_{\infty 1}-\bar{Z}_{01})}=\bar{Z}_{\infty 1}-\sqrt{\bar{Z}_{\infty 1}(\bar{Z}_{\infty n}-\bar{Z}_{0n})}\,;\\ \bar{Z}_B&=\bar{Z}_{\infty n}-\sqrt{\bar{Z}_{\infty n}(\bar{Z}_{\infty 1}-\bar{Z}_{01})}=\bar{Z}_{\infty n}-\sqrt{\bar{Z}_{\infty 1}(\bar{Z}_{\infty n}-\bar{Z}_{0n})}\,,\end{aligned}\right\}\qquad(7)$$

where

$\bar{Z}_{01}$ is the input impedance of the equivalent four-pole network (or of the waveguide itself, as in Fig. 1a) across terminals *1* in the case of a short circuit across terminals n;

$\bar{Z}_{\infty 1}$ is the same, but for the case of an open circuit across terminals n;

$\bar{Z}_{0n}$ is the input impedance of the equivalent four-pole network (or of the waveguide itself) across terminals n in the case of a short circuit across terminals *1*;

$\bar{Z}_{\infty n}$ is the same, but for the case of an open circuit across terminals *1*.

Formulas (7) enable us to determine the arm impedances $\bar{Z}_A$, $\bar{Z}_B$, $\bar{Z}_C$ of the equivalent quadripole, when the open-circuit and short-circuit input impedances of the nonhomogeneous waveguide under study are known.

Determination of the input impedances in the short-circuited case and in the open-circuited case, for the nonhomogeneous waveguide, presents no great difficulties [2, 3] if the following waveguide parameters are known

$$\bar{q}_{01};\ \bar{q}_{02}\ldots\bar{q}_{0n};\ \bar{W}_1;\ \bar{W}_2\ldots\bar{W}_n;\ l_1;\ l_2\ldots l_n.$$

Accordingly, with the arm impedances of the equivalent four-pole network and its loads, which may also be quadripole networks, known, we can always determine, with the aid of the equations for the unbalanced four-pole network, for example (cf. [2], p. 92), the integral propagation constants of the nonhomogeneous waveguide.

The integral propagation constants $\vec{S}_T$ and $\vec{S}_V$ determine the external wave properties of a nonhomogeneous waveguide, enabling us in the final analysis to find the mean velocity, which we term the integral velocity of the waves over any finite baseline x of a nonhomogeneous waveguide, and the attenuation suffered by the waves over the same baseline.

The mean (integral) velocity to be determined here will not be equal, in the general case, to the known mean velocity determined previously in seismic exploratory operations [15, 16]. This is to be explained by the dependence of the integral (true) velocity on the relationships of the wave impedances of the media (of the homogeneous sections of the waveguide). We shall return to this question at several points in the subsequent discussion.

The Differential Propagation Constant

To facilitate the study of the internal wave properties of a nonhomogeneous waveguide (Fig. 1), we introduce the concept of the differential propagation constant $\vec{D}$. The differential propagation constant is defined here as the limit which the ratio $\frac{\vec{S}}{\Delta x}$ approaches as the length of a homogeneous waveguide section Δx, having a propagation constant $\vec{S}$, approaches zero.

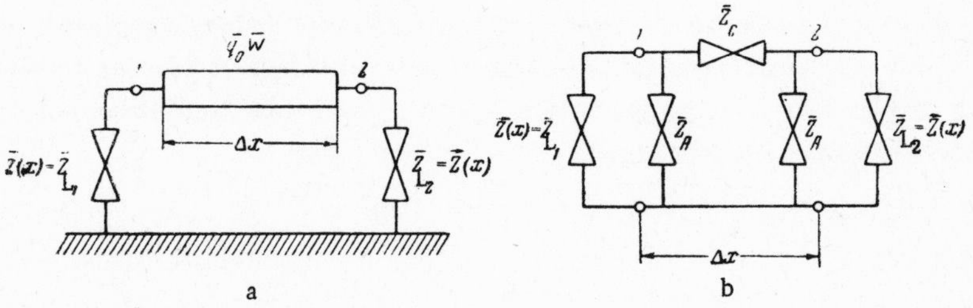

Fig. 2. An elemental homogeneous section (a) arbitrarily cut out of a waveguide such as depicted in Fig. 1a, and its equivalent four-pole network representation (b).

Figure 2a shows a section of homogeneous waveguide Δx arbitrarily cut out of a nonhomogeneous waveguide (cf. Fig. 1a), while Fig. 2b presents the equivalent balanced four-pole network[1]. The load impedances $\vec{Z}_{L_1}$ and $\vec{Z}_{L_2}$ are the input impedances of the discarded sections of the nonhomogeneous waveguide.

[1] Since the section Δx of the waveguide is homogeneous, it may be represented, as we know, by a balanced four-pole network equivalent.

The arm impedances of the equivalent four-pole network are determined by means of (7):

$$\left.\begin{aligned} \bar{Z}_C &= \sqrt{\bar{Z}_\infty(\bar{Z}_\infty - \bar{Z}_0)} = \frac{\bar{W}}{\operatorname{sh} \bar{q}_0 \Delta x}; \\ \bar{Z}_A &= \bar{Z}_\infty - \sqrt{\bar{Z}_\infty(\bar{Z}_\infty - \bar{Z}_0)} = \bar{W}\left(\frac{1}{\operatorname{th} \bar{q}_0 \Delta x} - \frac{1}{\operatorname{sh} \bar{q}_0 \Delta x}\right), \end{aligned}\right\} \quad (8)$$

where we make use of the values of the input impedances $\bar{Z}_0$ and $\bar{Z}_\infty$, known in the theory of electrical transmission lines:

$$\left.\begin{aligned} \bar{Z}_0 &= \bar{W} \cdot \operatorname{th} \bar{q}_0 \Delta x, \\ \bar{Z}_\infty &= \bar{W} \cdot \operatorname{cth} \bar{q}_0 \Delta x. \end{aligned}\right\} \quad (9)$$

Assuming the values of the input terminal impedances $\vec{Z}_{L_1}$ and $\vec{Z}_{L_2}$, presented to the four-pole network to be known, and with the arms impedances known, we may determine the network propagation constant for pressure waves and velocity waves.

In order to determine the propagation constant of a velocity wave in the case of an equivalent four-pole network (Fig. 2b) loaded with arbitrary, but known, impedances, the ratio of the input and output values of the velocity, i.e., $\bar{V}_1$ and $\bar{V}_2$ respectively, must be found. On the basis of the Kirchhoff circuit laws, the equivalent mechanical four-pole network may be computed with ease by finding the ratios of the input and output values of displacement velocity for waves propagating from left to right:

$$\frac{\bar{V}_1}{\bar{V}_2} = \frac{\bar{Z}_A + \bar{Z}_C + \vec{Z}_{L_2}}{\bar{Z}_C}. \quad (10)$$

The propagation constant of a velocity wave is found by taking the logarithm of (10):

$$\vec{S}_V = \ln\left(\frac{\bar{V}_1}{\bar{V}_2}\right) = \ln\left(\frac{\bar{Z}_A + \bar{Z}_C + \vec{Z}_{L_2}}{\bar{Z}_C}\right). \quad (11)$$

Substituting the values of the arm impedances in the four-pole network (8), we obtain the propagation constant of the velocity wave propagating down a homogeneous waveguide section of length Δx , loaded with an arbitrary impedance $\vec{Z}_{L_2}$ (cf. Fig. 2):

$$\vec{S}_V = \ln\left(\operatorname{ch} \bar{q}_0 \Delta x + \frac{\vec{Z}_{L_2}}{\bar{W}} \operatorname{sh} \bar{q}_0 \Delta x\right). \quad (12)$$

The propagation constant of a velocity wave (Fig. 2b) for the reverse direction of travel of the wave in a four-pole network may be determined in similar fashion:

$$\overleftarrow{S}_V = \ln\left(\frac{\bar{Z}_A + \bar{Z}_C + \bar{Z}_{L_1}}{\bar{Z}_C}\right) = \ln\left(\operatorname{ch}\bar{q}_0\Delta x + \frac{\overleftarrow{Z}_{L_1}}{\overline{W}}\operatorname{sh}\bar{q}_0\Delta x\right), \tag{13}$$

i.e., $\vec{S}_V$ and $\overleftarrow{S}_V$ are dependent on the impedances of the arms of the equivalent four-pole network or on the parameters of the waveguide $\bar{q}_0$; $\overline{W}$; Δx and on the load impedance of that end of the waveguide section toward which the wave is propagating.

The differential propagation constant of a velocity wave is written, according to the definition given above, in the following form

$$\vec{D}_V = \lim_{\Delta x \to 0} \frac{\vec{S}_V}{\Delta x} = \lim\left[\frac{\ln\left(\operatorname{ch}\bar{q}_0\Delta x + \frac{\vec{Z}_{L_2}}{\overline{W}}\operatorname{sh}\bar{q}_0\Delta x\right)}{\Delta x}\right]. \tag{14}$$

According to l'Hôpital's rule, by evaluating the indeterminate form we get

$$\vec{D}_V = \bar{q}_0 \frac{\vec{Z}_{L_2}}{\overline{W}}, \tag{15}$$

or, ultimately, the differential propagation constant for the instantaneous point x of some kth homogeneous waveguide section (cf. Fig. 1a):

$$\vec{D}_V(x) = \bar{q}_{0k} \frac{\vec{Z}(x)}{\overline{W}_k}, \tag{16}$$

where $\vec{Z}(x)$ is the input impedance of the waveguide for the instantaneous point x.

Similarly, we find, for the wave in the opposite direction

$$\overleftarrow{D}_V = \lim_{\Delta x \to 0} \frac{\overleftarrow{S}_V}{\Delta x} = \bar{q}\frac{\overleftarrow{Z}_{L_1}}{\overline{W}}, \tag{17}$$

or for the instantaneous point x of the kth homogeneous guide section:

$$\overleftarrow{D}_V(x) = \bar{q}_{0k} \frac{\overleftarrow{Z}(x)}{\overline{W}_k}. \tag{18}$$

The propagation constant of a pressure wave for the same four-pole network (Fig. 2) is determined from the formula

$$\vec{S}_T = \ln\frac{\overline{T}_1}{\overline{T}_2} = \ln\frac{\overline{V}_1 \cdot \bar{Z}_1}{\overline{V}_2 \vec{Z}_{L_2}}, \tag{19}$$

so that $\overline{T}_1=\overline{V}_1\vec{Z}_1$, and $\overline{T}_2=\overline{V}_2\vec{Z}_{L_2}$, where $\vec{Z}_1$ is the input impedance of the four-pole network across terminals *1*. The impedance $\vec{Z}_1$ may be represented in terms of the load impedance $\vec{Z}_{L_2}$ and the parameters of the homogeneous waveguide section (cf. [2, 8]):

$$\vec{Z}_1=\overline{W}\frac{\vec{Z}_{L_2}+\overline{W}\,\mathrm{th}\,\overline{q}_0\Delta x}{\overline{W}+\vec{Z}_{L_2}\cdot\mathrm{th}\,\overline{q}_0\Delta x}. \tag{20}$$

Substituting the value of $\vec{Z}_1$ into (19), and also replacing the ratio $\frac{\overline{V}_1}{\overline{V}_2}$ by (10), we obtain the expression for $\vec{S}_T$ as follows:

$$\vec{S}_T=\ln\left[\left(\frac{\overline{Z}_A+\overline{Z}_C+\vec{Z}_{L_2}}{\overline{Z}_C}\right)\left(\frac{\vec{Z}_{L_2}+\overline{W}\,\mathrm{th}\,\overline{q}_0\Delta x}{\overline{W}+\vec{Z}_{L_2}\,\mathrm{th}\,q_0\Delta x}\right)\cdot\frac{\overline{W}}{\vec{Z}_{L_2}}\right], \tag{21}$$

or, by replacing the values of $\overline{Z}_A$ and $\overline{Z}_C$ with (8), after cumbersome algebraic transformations, we arrive at the propagation constant of the pressures in a homogeneous waveguide section loaded with an arbitrary impedance $\overline{Z}_{L_2}$:

$$\vec{S}_T=\ln\left(\mathrm{ch}\,\overline{q}_0\Delta x+\frac{\overline{W}}{\vec{Z}_{L_2}}\,\mathrm{sh}\,q_0\Delta x\right). \tag{22}$$

Similar means serve to find, for the wave going in the opposite direction:

$$\overleftarrow{S}_T=\ln\left(\frac{\overline{T}'_2}{\overline{T}'_1}\right)=\ln\frac{\overline{V}'_2}{\overline{V}'_1}\cdot\frac{\overleftarrow{Z}_2}{\overleftarrow{Z}_{L_1}}=\ln\left(\mathrm{ch}\,q_0\Delta x+\frac{\overline{W}}{\overleftarrow{Z}_{L_1}}\,\mathrm{sh}\,\overline{q}_0\Delta x\right). \tag{23a}$$

The differential propagation constant of the pressure wave, by definition, is

$$\vec{D}_T=\lim_{\Delta x\to 0}\frac{\vec{S}_T}{\Delta x};\quad \overleftarrow{D}_T=\lim_{\Delta x\to 0}\frac{\overleftarrow{S}_T}{\Delta x}. \tag{23b}$$

Substituting into those equations the values of $\vec{S}_T$ and $\overleftarrow{S}_T$, i.e., (22) and (23a), and proceeding to the limit (evaluating the indeterminate form involved), we obtain

$$\left.\begin{aligned}\vec{D}_T&=\lim_{\Delta x\to 0}\left[\frac{\ln\left(\mathrm{ch}\,\overline{q}_0\Delta x+\frac{\overline{W}}{\vec{Z}_{L_2}}\,\mathrm{sh}\,\overline{q}_0\Delta x\right)}{\Delta x}\right]=\frac{\overline{W}}{\vec{Z}_{L_2}}\,\overline{q}_0;\\ \overleftarrow{D}_T&=\lim\left[\frac{\ln\left(\mathrm{ch}\,\overline{q}_0\Delta x+\frac{W}{\overleftarrow{Z}_{L_1}}\,\mathrm{sh}\,\overline{q}_0\Delta x\right)}{\Delta x}\right]=\frac{\overline{W}}{\overleftarrow{Z}_{L_1}}\,\overline{q}_0,\end{aligned}\right\} \tag{24}$$

or, ultimately, the differential propagation constants of the pressure wave for the kth homogeneous guide section (Fig. 1a) and for the instantaneous point x:

$$\vec{D}_T(x) = \frac{\overline{W}_k}{\vec{Z}(x)}\bar{q}_{0k}; \quad \overleftarrow{D}_T = \frac{\overline{W}_k}{\overleftarrow{Z}(x)}\bar{q}_{0k}, \tag{25}$$

where $\vec{Z}(x)$ and $\overleftarrow{Z}(x)$ are the input impedances of the discarded waveguide sections, for the instantaneous point x.

The differential propagation constants so obtained for the pressure and velocity waves may also be determined from the basic equations of the homogeneous waveguide (mechanical transmission line). This requires finding the ratios $\frac{\overline{V}_1}{\overline{V}_2}$ and $\frac{\overline{T}_1}{\overline{T}_2}$, and then taking the logarithm of those ratios, after which we proceed out to the limit at $\Delta x \to 0$.

It is no great difficulty to find the differential propagation constant of the intensity wave [cf. (1b)]:

$$\vec{D}_Q = \lim_{\Delta x \to 0} \frac{\frac{1}{2}(\vec{S}_V + \vec{S}_T)}{\Delta x} = \frac{1}{2}\left(\lim_{\Delta x \to 0}\frac{\vec{S}_V}{\Delta x} + \lim_{\Delta x \to 0}\frac{\vec{S}_T}{\Delta x}\right) = \frac{1}{2}(D_V(x) + D_T(x)). \tag{26}$$

We substitute the values of the differential propagation constants of the velocity and pressure waves (16) and (25); finally, we obtain:

$$\vec{D}_Q = \frac{\overline{W}^2 + \vec{Z}^2(x)}{2\overline{W} \cdot \vec{Z}(x)} \cdot \bar{q}_0. \tag{27}$$

Similarly, for the transmission in the reverse direction, we get:

$$\overleftarrow{D}_Q = \frac{\overline{W}^2 + \overleftarrow{Z}^2(x)}{2\overline{W} \cdot \overleftarrow{Z}(x)} \bar{q}_0. \tag{28}$$

Accordingly, with the parameters $\bar{q}_0$, $\overline{W}$ and l of the waveguide proper known, for the waveguide in which the differential propagation constants are being determined, and with the load impedances $\vec{Z}_{L_2}$ and $\overleftarrow{Z}_{L_1}$, which constitute the input terminal impedances of adjacent waveguides, also known, we can always find $\vec{D}_V(x)$, $\vec{D}_T(x)$ and $\vec{D}_Q(x)$ for the corresponding homogeneous waveguide sections (cf. Fig. 1a).

The Relationship between the Integral and the Differential Propagation Constants

A knowledge of the differential propagation constants $\vec{D}_V$ and $\vec{D}_T$ for discrete homogeneous sections of a nonhomogeneous waveguide makes it possible to determine the integral propagation constants of a nonhomogeneous waveguide as a whole by means of integrating. Actually, since the differential propagation constant $\vec{D}_V$ of an elemental section of waveguide of length dx is, by definition:

$$D_V = \lim_{\Delta x \to 0} \left[\frac{\ln\left(\frac{\bar{V}_{\text{in}}}{\bar{V}_{\text{out}}}\right)}{\Delta x} \right],$$

and the integral propagation constant of the entire nonhomogeneous waveguide consisting of n homogeneous sections

$$\vec{S}_V = \ln \frac{\bar{V}_1}{\bar{V}_{n+1}},$$

then, taking the summation of the products $\vec{D}_V\, dx$ over the entire nonhomogeneous waveguide, we obtain its integral propagation constant

$$\vec{S}_V = dx \cdot \lim_{\Delta x \to 0} \left[\frac{\ln\left(\frac{\bar{V}_1}{\bar{V}_2}\right)}{\Delta x} \right] + dx \cdot \lim_{\Delta x \to 0} \left[\frac{\ln\left(\frac{\bar{V}_2}{\bar{V}_3}\right)}{\Delta x} \right] + \ldots + dx \cdot \lim_{\Delta x \to 0} \left[\frac{\ln \frac{\bar{V}_n}{\bar{V}_{n+1}}}{\Delta x} \right], \quad \text{(29a)}$$

where $\bar{V}_1$, $\bar{V}_2$, $\bar{V}_3 \ldots \bar{V}_{n+1}$ are the values of the velocity waves at points of contact between elemental waveguide sections.

We now replace the sum of the limits by the limit of the sum:

$$\vec{S}_V = \lim \frac{\Delta x}{\Delta x} \left[\ln\left(\frac{\bar{V}_1}{\bar{V}_2}\right) + \ln\left(\frac{\bar{V}_2}{\bar{V}_3}\right) + \ldots + \ln\left(\frac{\bar{V}_n}{\bar{V}_{n+1}}\right) \right] = \ln\left(\frac{\bar{V}_1 \cdot \bar{V}_2 \cdot \ldots \bar{V}_n}{\bar{V}_2 \cdot \bar{V}_3 \cdot \ldots \bar{V}_{n+1}} \right) = \ln\left(\frac{\bar{V}_1}{\bar{V}_{n+1}}\right), \quad \text{(29b)}$$

which is what required proof. Similar reasoning may be applied to $\vec{S}_T$. The integral propagation constants for a nonhomogeneous waveguide (Fig. 1a) are written in the following manner:

$$\vec{S}_V = \int_{x_1}^{x_2} \vec{D}_{V_1} dx + \int_{x_2}^{x_3} \vec{D}_{V_2} dx + \ldots + \int_{x_{n-1}}^{x_n} \vec{D}_{V_{n-1}} dx + \int_{x_n}^{x_{n+1}} \vec{D}_{V_n} dx; \quad (29c)$$

$$\vec{S}_T = \int_{x_1}^{x_2} \vec{D}_{T_1} dx + \int_{x_2}^{x_3} \vec{D}_{T_2} dx + \ldots + \int_{x_{n-1}}^{x_n} \vec{D}_{T_{n-1}} dx + \int_{x_n}^{x_{n+1}} \vec{D}_{T_n} dx; \quad (30)$$

where, respectively:

$$\vec{D}_{V_1} = \frac{\vec{Z}_1(x)}{\overline{W}_1} \bar{q}_{01} \Big|_{x_1 \leqslant x \leqslant x_2}; \; \vec{D}_{V_2} = \frac{\vec{Z}_2(x)}{\overline{W}_2} q_{02} \Big|_{x_2 \leqslant x \leqslant x_3}; \ldots;$$

$$\vec{D}_{V_n} = \frac{\vec{Z}_n(x)}{\overline{W}_n} \bar{q}_{0n} \Big|_{x_n \leqslant x \leqslant x_{n+1}}, \quad (31)$$

$$\vec{D}_{T_1} = \frac{\overline{W}_1}{\vec{Z}_1(x)} \bar{q}_{01} \Big|_{x_1 \leqslant x \leqslant x_2}; \; \vec{D}_{T_2} = \frac{\overline{W}_2}{\vec{Z}_2(x)} \cdot \bar{q}_{02} \Big|_{x_2 \leqslant x \leqslant x_3}; \ldots;$$

$$\vec{D}_{T_n} = \frac{\overline{W}_n}{\vec{Z}_2(x)} \bar{q}_{0n} \Big|_{x_n \leqslant x \leqslant x_{n+1}}, \quad (32)$$

and $\vec{Z}_1(x)$; $\vec{Z}_2(x)$; $\vec{Z}_3(x)$ . . . $\vec{Z}_n(x)$ are the input terminal impedances of the corresponding waveguide sections, are dependent on the parameters of the nonhomogeneous waveguide, and are subject to determination below.

In (29c) and (30), each discrete integral is an integral propagation constant of the respective homogeneous sections of a nonhomogeneous waveguide, and the sum of the integrals gives us the integral propagation constant of the entire nonhomogeneous waveguide.

The method of differential propagation constants enables us to study the wave phenomena not only in piecewise homogeneous waveguides, but also in waveguides with smoothly varying parameters $\bar{q}_0(x)$ and $\overline{W}(x)$. For this purpose, representing such a waveguide by successively inserted and infinitesimally small homogeneous sections and assuming the parameters $\bar{q}_0$ and $\overline{W}$ to be varying in response to variation in x, in correspondence with known laws governing the guide parameters $\bar{q}_0(x)$ and $\overline{W}(x)$, we find, in the final analysis, the following differential propagation constants of the waveguide under study:

$$\vec{D}_V(x) = \frac{\vec{Z}(x)}{\overline{W}(x)} \bar{q}_0(x); \; \vec{D}_T(x) = \frac{\overline{W}(x)}{\vec{Z}(x)} \bar{q}_0(x), \quad (33)$$

where $\vec{Z}(x)$ is the input impedance of that end of the elemental waveguide section with continuously varying parameters toward which the wave is traveling. The input impedance $\vec{Z}(x)$ also is subject to determination in the further discussion.

The integral propagation constant of the waveguide in question is determined in the following manner:

$$\vec{S}_V = \int_{x_k}^{x_{k+1}} \vec{D}_V(x)\,dx; \quad \vec{S}_T = \int_{x_k}^{x_{k+1}} \vec{D}_T(x)\,dx, \tag{34}$$

where $x_k - x_{k+1}$ is the waveguide interval under investigation.

Substituting into (34) the values of $\vec{D}_V$ and $\vec{D}_T$, we get

$$\vec{S}_V = \int_{x_k}^{x_{k+1}} \frac{\vec{Z}(x)}{\overline{W}(x)} \bar{q}_0(x)\,dx; \quad \vec{S}_T = \int_{x_k}^{x_{k+1}} \frac{\overline{W}(x)}{\vec{Z}(x)} \bar{q}_0(x)\,dx, \tag{35}$$

where $\vec{Z}(x)$; $\overline{W}(x)$ and $\bar{q}_0(x)$ are in the general case functions of x and of the Heaviside operator p.

In conclusion, note that if a nonhomogeneous waveguide (Fig. 1a) has sections $x_k - x_{k+1}$, where the waveguide parameters vary continuously, i.e., $\bar{q}_0(x)$ and $\overline{W}(x)$ vary continuously, then, in determining the integral propagation constants of the entire waveguide, the corresponding integrals in (29) and (30) must be replaced by the integrals in (34).

The formulas so obtained for the differential propagation constants in (16), (18), (25), (27), (28), are the initial values to be considered in studying the microstructure of the waves in nonhomogeneous waveguides (in principle, at any degree of complexity). In turn, the formulas for the integral propagation constants, (29) and (30), make it possible to investigate the macrostructure of the waves in the same waveguides. In order to determine fully the differential and integral propagation constants in terms of the waveguide parameters, the relationship between the input impedances $\overleftarrow{Z}(x)$ and $\vec{Z}(x)$ and the parameters $\bar{q}_0$, $\overline{W}$ and l must be found. We shall now proceed to determine them.

SECTION TWO

DETERMINATION OF THE INPUT IMPEDANCES OF A NONHOMOGENEOUS WAVEGUIDE

As follows from the preceding paragraph, in order to determine fully the differential propagation constants $\vec{D}_V$ and $\vec{D}_T$, we have to find the input impedances $\vec{Z}(x)$ of the nonhomogeneous waveguide, i.e., express them in terms of the guide parameters $\bar{q}_0$, $\bar{W}$ and l, which we shall assume to be known.

We are aware, from [2], of the fact that the input impedances of nonhomogeneous waveguides may be determined by the method of successive elimination of sections of homogeneous waveguides, beginning with that end of the nonhomogeneous waveguide toward which the elastic wave is advancing.

Let us determine, for some instantaneous point x in a nonhomogeneous waveguide (Fig. 1a), the input impedance $\vec{Z}(x)$, beginning with the guide section furthest out to the right. The input impedance of the n th homogeneous section is determined, for the instantaneous point x, as follows:

$$\vec{Z}_n(x) = \bar{W}_n \frac{\bar{Z}_{L\,n+1} + \bar{W}_n \operatorname{th}(x_{n+1} - x)\,\bar{q}_{0n}}{\bar{Z}_{L\,n+1} \cdot \operatorname{th}(x_{n+1} - x)\,\bar{q}_{0n} + \bar{W}_n}\Bigg|_{x_n \leqslant x \leqslant x_{n+1}} \tag{36}$$

For the case where x is equal to x_n, we obtain the input impedance of the entire homogeneous section of waveguide $l_n = x_{n+1} - x_n$ at the point x_n:

$$\vec{Z}_n = \bar{W}_n \frac{\bar{Z}_{L\,n+1} + \bar{W}_n \operatorname{th} l_n \bar{q}_{0n}}{\bar{Z}_{L\,n+1} \cdot \operatorname{th} l_n \bar{q}_{0n} + \bar{W}_n}. \tag{37}$$

Having determined the input impedance of the entire nth homogeneous section, we shall now assume it to constitute the load on the following $(n-1)$th homogeneous section. Then, the input impedance of that $(n-1)$th section, for the instantaneous point x, is determined in similar fashion:

$$\vec{Z}_{n-1}(x)=\overline{W}_{n-1}\left.\frac{\vec{Z}_n+\overline{W}_{n-1}\,\mathrm{th}\,(x_n-x)\,\bar{q}_{0(n-1)}}{\vec{Z}_n\cdot\mathrm{th}\,(x_n-x)\bar{q}_{0(n-1)}+\overline{W}_{n-1}}\right|_{x_{n-1}\leqslant x\leqslant x_n} \tag{38}$$

When x takes on the value of x_{n-1}, we obtain the input impedance of the entire $(n-1)$th homogeneous waveguide section of length $l_{n-1}=x_n-x_{n-1}$, terminating in the impedance $\vec{Z}_n$:

$$\vec{Z}_{n-1}=\overline{W}_{n-1}\frac{\vec{Z}_n+\overline{W}_{n-1}\,\mathrm{th}\,l_{n-1}\bar{q}_{0(n-1)}}{\vec{Z}_n\,\mathrm{th}\,l_{n-1}\bar{q}_{0(n-1)}+\overline{W}_{n-1}} \tag{39}$$

and so forth. The input impedance of the last section in the transmission line, i.e., the first section, for the instantaneous point x, will equal

$$\vec{Z}_{1(x)}=\overline{W}_1\left.\frac{\vec{Z}_2+\overline{W}_1\,\mathrm{th}\,(x_2-x)\,\bar{q}_{01}}{\vec{Z}_2\cdot\mathrm{th}\,(x_2-x)\bar{q}_{01}+\overline{W}_1}\right|_{x_1\leqslant x\leqslant x_2}, \tag{40}$$

and the input impedance of the entire homogeneous section of the waveguide $l_1=x_2-x_1$ or, what amounts to the same thing, the input impedance of the entire nonhomogeneous waveguide $l=x_{n+1}-x_1$ at the point x_1:

$$\vec{Z}_1=\overline{W}_1\frac{\vec{Z}_2+\overline{W}_1\,\mathrm{th}\,l_1\bar{q}_{01}}{\vec{Z}_2\cdot\mathrm{th}\,l_1\bar{q}_{01}+\overline{W}_1}. \tag{41}$$

Accordingly, we have the set of equations (37, 39, 41), which enables us to determine the input impedances for the fixed points of contact between homogeneous waveguide sections x_n ; x_{n-1} . . . x_2; x_1.

Having determined, for those points, the input impedances $\vec{Z}_n$; $\vec{Z}_{n-1}$ . . . $\vec{Z}_2$, which are independent of the variable x, we may now substitute them, respectively, into the system of equations (36), (38) and (40), and find the unknown input impedances of the homogeneous waveguide sections $\vec{Z}_n(x)$; $\vec{Z}_{n-1}(x)$ . . . $\vec{Z}_1(x)$ for the instantaneous coordinate x.

Waveguides with Smoothly Varying Parameters

The wave phenomena in waveguides (homogeneous media) with smoothly varying parameters have been discussed by a number of authors [17, 18, 19]. The solution of the problem as treated in the papers referred to was attained with the aid of the wave equation with variable coefficients, under the assumption that no absorption takes place in the medium involved. The solution proposed here to that problem is based on the use of the differential propagation constant, and has several advantages: 1) the problem, at its most difficult part, reduces to a conventional first-order equation (of the Riccati type) whose solution is the input impedance of the waveguide; 2) as intermediate links in the solution, the differential propagation constants $\vec{D}_V(x)$ and $\vec{D}_T(x)$, which enable us to investigate the microstructure of the waves in the waveguide, are determined; 3) the entire course of the solution is intimately associated with the physical aspect of the wave process in the waveguide.

Consider a waveguide with smoothly varying parameters $\bar{q}_0(x)$; $\overline{W}(x)$. As already stated, that type of waveguide is represented here as the limiting case of a waveguide consisting of successively inserted small homogeneous sections of length Δx, differing from each other in their parameters $\bar{q}_0$, $\overline{W}$, according to some specified law $\bar{q}_0(x)$, $\overline{W}(x)$. For each homogeneous section of waveguide, the input impedance may be written in the following form (similar to the system of equations 37, 39, 41):

$$\vec{Z}(x)=\overline{W}(x)\,\frac{\vec{Z}(x+\Delta x)+\overline{W}(x)\,\mathrm{th}\,\bar{q}_0(x)\,\Delta x}{\vec{Z}(x+\Delta x)\,\mathrm{th}\,\bar{q}_0(x)\,\Delta x+\overline{W}(x)}, \tag{42}$$

where $\vec{Z}(x)$ is the input impedance of the homogeneous section Δx; $\vec{Z}(x+\Delta x)$ is the input impedance of the homogeneous section to the right (the direction of wave propagation and the abscissa being from left to right). Before proceeding to the limit, let us transform (42)

$$[\vec{Z}(x)\cdot\vec{Z}(x+\Delta x)-\overline{W}^2(x)]\,\mathrm{th}\,\bar{q}_0(x)\,\Delta x=\overline{W}(x)\,[\vec{Z}(x+\Delta x)-\vec{Z}(x)]. \tag{43}$$

Divide through by Δx and proceed to the limit $\Delta x\to 0$:

$$\lim_{\Delta x\to 0}\frac{[\vec{Z}(x)\,\vec{Z}(x+\Delta x)-W^2(x)]\,\mathrm{th}\,\bar{q}_0(x)\,\Delta x}{\Delta x}=\overline{W}(x)\lim_{\Delta x\to 0}\frac{\vec{Z}(x+\Delta x)-\vec{Z}(x)}{\Delta x}. \tag{44}$$

Evaluating the indeterminate form in the left hand member of the equation, we have:

$$[\vec{Z}^2(x)-\overline{W}^2(x)]\,\bar{q}_0(x)=\overline{W}(x)\,\frac{d\vec{Z}(x)}{dx}. \tag{45}$$

Solving for the derivative, we eventually obtain a differential equation of the Riccati type:

$$\frac{d\vec{Z}(x)}{dx}=\frac{\bar{q}_0(x)}{\overline{W}(x)}\vec{Z}^2(x)-q_0(x)\overline{W}(x), \tag{46}$$

or

$$y'=y^2\frac{\bar{q}_0(x)}{\overline{W}(x)}-\bar{q}_0(x)\overline{W}(x), \tag{47}$$

where we have, by definition, $y=\vec{Z}(x)$.

In order to find, at some instantaneous point x, the input impedance of a waveguide having smoothly varying and arbitrarily assigned parameters $\bar{q}_0(x)$ and $\overline{W}(x)$, we have to solve that non-linear first-order equation.

Consider the simplest particular case of a waveguide with $\bar{q}_0=f(x)$ and $\overline{W}=\text{const}$. It follows, from physical considerations, that if all elemental homogeneous waveguide sections (of length dx) have the same wave impedance $\overline{W}$, in other words if $\overline{W}$ does not vary with the distance x, then the waveguide input terminal impedance $\vec{Z}(x)$ must be constant and equal to $\overline{W}$ for any relation governing the parameter $\bar{q}_0(x)$. Actually, if we assume $\overline{W}$ is constant, i.e., independent of x, the differential equation (47) will then take on the following form:

$$y'=y^2\frac{\bar{q}_0(x)}{\overline{W}}-\bar{q}_0(x)\overline{W}. \tag{48}$$

Its solution will be $y=\pm W$ for any pattern of variation in $\bar{q}_0(x)$. Accordingly, for any value of x, the input impedance is $\vec{Z}(x)=\overline{W}$. The integral propagation constant of that waveguide will be, according to (35):

$$\left.\begin{aligned}\vec{S}_V&=\int\frac{\overline{W}}{\overline{W}}\bar{q}_0(x)\,dx=\int\bar{q}_0(x)\,dx;\\ \vec{S}_T&=\int\frac{\overline{W}}{\overline{W}}\bar{q}_0(x)\,dx=\int\bar{q}_0(x)\,dx.\end{aligned}\right\} \tag{49}$$

For a medium without loss, the parameter $\bar{q}_0(x)$ is expressed in terms of the velocity of propagation as follows:

$$\bar{q}_0(x)=\frac{p}{c(x)}=\frac{p}{\sqrt{\frac{K_0(x)}{M_0(x)}}}, \tag{50}$$

where p is the Heaviside operator; $c=c(x)$ is a specified relation governing the velocity of propagation. Substituting (50) in (49), we get:

$$\vec{S}_V=p\int\frac{dx}{c(x)}=\vec{S}_T, \tag{51}$$

i.e., we end up with the case where the laws of geometric seismics [16] retain their validity. In other cases, i.e., where the wave impedance is a function of x, the velocity will be dependent on the relation governing variation in $\overline{W}(x)$.

We may assign a number of patterns of variation in the parameters of acoustical waveguides $\bar{q}_0(x)$ and $\overline{W}(x)$ of interest in seismology and seismic prospecting (with resistive losses neglected), taking as known the fact that $\bar{q}_0(x)$ characterizes at each point (for infinitesimally small wavelengths) the reciprocal of the velocity $c(x)=\sqrt{\frac{K_0(x)}{M_0(x)}}$, while $\overline{W}(x)$ is the wave impedance (acoustical stiffness):

1. The propagation constant and the wave impedance of the waveguide, as a function of the first power of the distance x:

$$\bar{q}_0(x)=\frac{\bar{q}_0}{x}; \quad \overline{W}(x)=x\overline{W}, \tag{52}$$

where $\bar{q}_0$ and $\overline{W}$ are not dependent on x and are assigned known values. Then, the input impedance for the instantaneous point x is determined from the equation:

$$y'=\frac{\bar{q}_0}{\overline{W}}x^{-2}\cdot y^2-\overline{W}\bar{q}_0. \tag{53}$$

2. The waveguide parameters vary in obedience to an exponential law:

$$\bar{q}_0(x)=\bar{q}_0e^{-\alpha x}; \quad \overline{W}(x)=\overline{W}\cdot e^{\beta x}, \tag{54}$$

whereupon we have the following equation for determining the input impedance of the waveguide $y=\vec{Z}(x)$:

$$y'=\frac{\bar{q}_0}{\overline{W}}e^{-x(\alpha+\beta)}\cdot y^2-\bar{q}_0\cdot\overline{W}\cdot e^{x(\beta-\alpha)}. \tag{55}$$

3. The waveguide parameters vary according to some periodic pattern:

$$\bar{q}_0(x)=\bar{q}_0-\bar{q}_{0A}\sin\frac{2\pi}{\lambda}x;\quad \bar{W}(x)=\bar{W}+\bar{W}_A\sin\frac{2\pi}{\lambda}x, \tag{56}$$

where λ is the period of nonuniformity of the waveguide (of the homogeneous medium). The equation defining the input impedance $\vec{Z}(x)$ is written in the following form:

$$y'=\frac{\bar{q}_0-\bar{q}_{0A}\sin\frac{2\pi}{\lambda}x}{\bar{W}+\bar{W}_A\sin\frac{2\pi}{\lambda}x}y^2-\left(\bar{q}_0-\bar{q}_{0A}\sin\frac{2\pi}{\lambda}x\right)\left(\bar{W}+\bar{W}_A\sin\frac{2\pi}{\lambda}x\right). \tag{57}$$

The solution of the Riccati differential equations (53, 55, 57), as we know [20, 21], runs up against sizable difficulties, and cannot be expressed in elementary functions, in the general case. However, there exists a series of Riccati equations whose solutions are obtained with comparative ease, in terms of elementary functions as well. As an example of the solution of a Riccati type equation, consider the case where the waveguide parameters vary in accordance with the following relationships:

$$\bar{q}_0(x)=\frac{\bar{q}_0}{x}=\frac{p}{\sqrt{\frac{K_0}{M_0\cdot x^{-2}}}}=\frac{p}{\sqrt{\frac{K_0}{\rho(x)}}}$$

and

$$\bar{W}(x)=\frac{\bar{W}}{x}=\sqrt{K_0(M_0\cdot x^{-2})}=\sqrt{K_0\rho(x)},$$

i.e., the waveguide density decreases according to the quadratic law $\rho=M_0\cdot x^{-2}$, and the elasticity $K_0=\text{const}$. Then, according to (47), we obtain the following equation for finding the input terminal impedance $\vec{Z}(x)$:

$$y'=\frac{\bar{q}_0}{\bar{W}}y^2-\bar{q}_0\cdot\bar{W}\cdot x^{-2}, \tag{58}$$

which constitutes a limiting form of the Riccati equation [21] solved in terms of elementary functions. Let us have recourse to the substitution of $y=\frac{v}{x}$, by which means equation (58) is reduced to:

$$x\frac{dv}{dx}=-\bar{q}_0\bar{W}+v+\frac{\bar{q}_0}{\bar{W}_0}v^2. \tag{59}$$

This is an equation with separable variables. Integrating:

$$\int \frac{dv}{\frac{\bar{q}_0}{\overline{W}} v^2 + v - \bar{q}_0 \overline{W}} = \int \frac{dx}{x}. \tag{60}$$

Making use of a table of integrals, and putting $a = \sqrt{1 + 4\bar{q}_0}$, we obtain:

$$-\frac{2}{a} \operatorname{arctg} \frac{2\frac{\bar{q}_0}{\overline{W}} v + 1}{a} = \ln x. \tag{61}$$

Substituting the value $v = x \cdot y$ and solving for y, we find the value of the waveguide input terminal impedance

$$\vec{Z}(x) = y = \frac{\overline{W}}{2\bar{q}_0 \cdot x}\left[-1 - a \operatorname{th}\left(\frac{a}{2} \ln x\right)\right]. \tag{62}$$

The differential propagation constants of the waveguide under study, according to (33), are equal to:

$$\left.\begin{aligned} \vec{D}_V(x) &= \frac{\vec{Z}(x)}{\overline{W}(x)} \bar{q}_0(x) = \frac{1}{2x}\left[-1 - a \operatorname{th}\left(\frac{a}{2} \ln x\right)\right] = f_V(p, x), \\ \vec{D}_T(x) &= \frac{\overline{W}(x)}{\vec{Z}(x)} \bar{q}_0(x) = \frac{2\bar{q}_0^2}{x}\left[-1 - a \operatorname{th}\left(\frac{a}{2} \ln x\right)\right]^{-1} = f_T(p, x), \end{aligned}\right\} \tag{63}$$

where $a = \sqrt{1 + 4\bar{q}_0}$.

With this, we conclude the investigation of the input terminal impedances of the waveguides. We now proceed to concrete wave problems for piecewise homogeneous waveguides.

SECTION THREE

INCIDENCE OF A PLANE WAVE NORMAL TO THE INTERFACE SEPARATING TWO ELASTIC HALF-SPACES

We shall now investigate the propagation of a plane wave normal to the flat boundary of a medium consisting of two homogeneous elastic half-spaces. This corresponds, as stated earlier, to the treatment of an acoustic waveguide (Fig. 3) arbitrarily cut out normal to the interface between two elastic half-spaces.

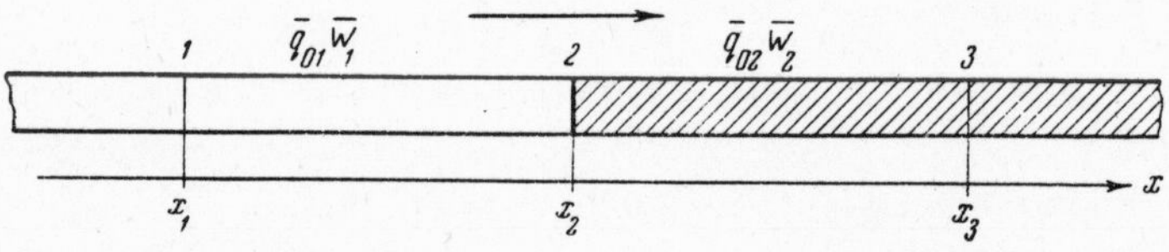

Fig. 3. An acoustical waveguide, arbitrarily cut out normal to the interface between two elastic half-spaces.

A similar problem, as we are well aware, has been subjected to study on more than one occasion, but the problems of the microstructure of the waves, even in that simplest of all cases, has not been clarified in the literature. In addition, it is natural to analyze the proposed method for solution of the wave problems in the simplest example, and to correlate the end solution for the integral wave characteristics with the known results.

Suppose that the media have losses, depending, for example, on viscosity: then the propagation constants $\bar{q}_0$ and the wave impedance $\bar{W}$ will assume the following values [22]:

$$\left.\begin{aligned} \bar{q}_{01} &= \frac{p}{c_1\sqrt{1+p\lambda_{K_1}}}, & \overline{W}_1 &= \sqrt{K_{01}\cdot M_{01}(1+p\lambda_{K_1})}, \\ \bar{q}_{02} &= \frac{p}{c_2\sqrt{1+p\lambda_{K_2}}}, & \overline{W}_2 &= \sqrt{K_{02}\cdot M_{02}(1+p\lambda_{K_2})}, \end{aligned}\right\} \tag{64}$$

where $\bar{q}_{01}$ and $\overline{W}_1$ denote the first medium, $\bar{q}_{02}$ and $\overline{W}_2$ denote the second medium: $c_1 = \sqrt{\frac{K_{01}}{M_{01}}}$; $c_2 = \sqrt{\frac{K_{02}}{M_{02}}}$; λ_{K_1} and λ_{K_2} are factors dependent on viscosity, and p is the Heaviside operator.

For the waves advancing from left to right, the differential propagation constants for the first medium are [cf. (2), (16) and (25)]:

$$\vec{D}_{1V} = \frac{\vec{Z}_1(x)}{\overline{W}_1}\cdot\bar{q}_{01}; \qquad \vec{D}_{1T} = \frac{\overline{W}_1}{\vec{Z}_1(x)}\cdot\bar{q}_{01}. \tag{65}$$

For the second medium, since its input impedances $\vec{Z}_2(x) = \overline{W}_2$, the differential propagation constants are $\vec{D}_{2V} = \vec{D}_{2T} = \bar{q}_0$.

The input impedance for the instantaneous point x in the first medium are determined, according to (40):

$$\vec{Z}_1(x) = \overline{W}_1 \frac{\overline{W}_2 + \overline{W}_1 \operatorname{th}\bar{q}_{01}(x_2 - x)}{\overline{W}_2 \operatorname{th}\bar{q}_{01}(x_2 - x) + \overline{W}_1}\bigg|_{-\infty\leqslant x\leqslant x_2} \tag{66}$$

[(cf. the graph (Fig. 4) of the input impedances $\vec{Z}_1(x)$, plotted according to (66), with $p = i\omega$ and $\lambda_{K_1} = \lambda_{K_2} = 0$]. We now substitute the input impedance in (66) into equations (65):

$$\left.\begin{aligned} \vec{D}_{1V} &= \frac{\overline{W}_2 + \overline{W}_1 \operatorname{th}\bar{q}_{01}(x_2 - x)}{\overline{W}_2 \operatorname{th}\bar{q}_{01}(x_2 - x) - \overline{W}_1}\,\bar{q}_{01} = f_V(x, p), \\ \vec{D}_{1T} &= \frac{\overline{W}_2 \operatorname{th}\bar{q}_{01}(x_2 - x) + \overline{W}_1}{\overline{W}_2 + W_1 \operatorname{th}\bar{q}_{01}(x_2 - x)}\,\bar{q}_{01} = f_T(x, p). \end{aligned}\right\} \tag{67}$$

The functions $f_V(x, p)$ and $f_T(x, p)$ enable us to determine the velocity and the attenuation factor of a transient wave over an infinitesimally small interval of a nonideal elastic waveguide. However, consider for the sake of simplicity an acoustical waveguide without loss ($\lambda_{K_1} = \lambda_{K_2} = 0$), observing the constraint that a steady-state sinusoidal wave is propagating down the waveguide (in that case, $p = i\omega$).

Then, equations (67) are written in the following manner:

$$\left.\begin{aligned}\vec{D}_{1V} &= \frac{i\omega}{c_1}\,\frac{W_2 + W_1\cdot \operatorname{th} i\dfrac{\omega}{c_1}(x_2 - x)}{W_2 \operatorname{th} i\dfrac{\omega}{c_1}(x_2 - x) + W_1} = f_V(x, \omega);\\ \vec{D}_{1T} &= \frac{i\omega}{c_1}\,\frac{W_2 \operatorname{th} i\dfrac{\omega}{c_1}(x_2 - x) + W_1}{W_2 + W_1 \operatorname{th} i\dfrac{\omega}{c_1}(x_2 - x)} = f_T(x, \omega),\end{aligned}\right\} \quad (68)$$

where $f_V(x, \omega)$ and $f_T(x, \omega)$ are complex functions of x and of the frequency ω, the real parts of which define the differential attenuation factor α', and the imaginary parts of which define the differential phase constants β' over an infinitesimally small waveguide section, for the corresponding pressure waves and velocity waves:

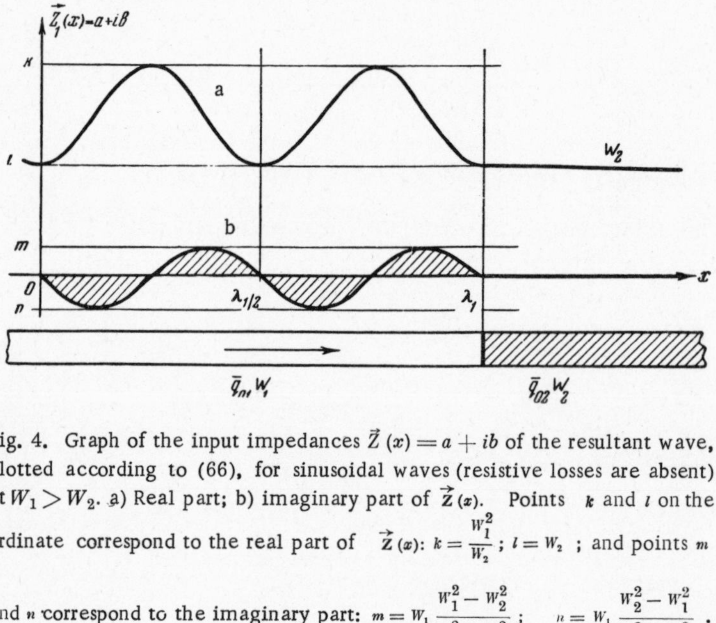

Fig. 4. Graph of the input impedances $\vec{Z}(x) = a + ib$ of the resultant wave, plotted according to (66), for sinusoidal waves (resistive losses are absent) at $W_1 > W_2$. a) Real part; b) imaginary part of $\vec{Z}(x)$. Points k and l on the ordinate correspond to the real part of $\vec{Z}(x)$: $k = \frac{W_1^2}{W_2}$; $l = W_2$; and points m and n correspond to the imaginary part: $m = W_1 \frac{W_1^2 - W_2^2}{W_1^2 + W^2}$; $n = W_1 \frac{W_2^2 - W_1^2}{W_1^2 + W_2^2}$.

$$\vec{D}_{1V} = \alpha'_{1V} + i\beta'_{1V}; \qquad \vec{D}_{1T} = \alpha'_{1T} + i\beta'_{1T}. \quad (69)$$

We determine the real and the imaginary parts of the complex quantities $\vec{D}_{1V}$ and $\vec{D}_{1T}$. For this, we replace the hyperbolic functions of the imaginary argument, in (68), by the trigonometric functions:

$$\left.\begin{aligned}\vec{D}_{1V}&=\frac{\omega}{c_1}\,\frac{iW_2-W_1\operatorname{tg}\frac{\omega}{c_1}(x_2-x_1)}{iW_2\operatorname{tg}\frac{\omega}{c_1}(x_2-x)+W_1};\\ \vec{D}_{1T}&=\frac{\omega}{c_1}\,\frac{-W_2\operatorname{tg}\frac{\omega}{c_1}(x_2-x_1)+iW_1}{W_2+iW_1\operatorname{tg}\frac{\omega}{c_1}(x_2-x)}.\end{aligned}\right\}\tag{70}$$

We then multiply the numerator and denominator by the complex number conjugate to the denominator, and separate the real and imaginary parts:

$$\begin{aligned}\vec{D}_{1V}=&\frac{k(1-n_{12}^2)\sin k_1(x_2-x_1)\cos k_1(x_2-x)}{\sin^2 k_1(x_2-x)+n_{12}^2\cos^2 k_1(x_2-x)}+\\ &+i\frac{k_1n_{12}}{\sin^2 k_1(x_2-x)+n_{12}^2\cos^2 k_1(x_2-x)},\end{aligned}\tag{71}$$

where $k_1=\frac{\omega}{c_1}=\frac{2\pi}{\lambda_1}$ is the wave number; $n_{12}=\frac{W_1}{W_2}$;

$$\begin{aligned}\vec{D}_{1T}=&\frac{k_1(1-n_{21}^2)\sin k_1(x_2-x)\cos k_1(x_2-x)}{\sin^2 k_1(x_2-x)+n_{21}^2\cos^2 k_1(x_2-x)}+\\ &+i\frac{k_1n_{21}}{\sin^2 k_1(x_2-x)+n_{21}^2\cos^2 k_1(x_2-x)},\end{aligned}\tag{72}$$

where $n_{21}=\frac{W_2}{W_1}$.

From (71) and (72), we obtain the differential attenuation coefficients and differential phase constants for the pressure waves α'_T ; β'_T , and the same for the velocity waves α'_V ; β'_V :

$$\left.\begin{aligned}\alpha'_{1V}&=\frac{k_1(1-n_{12}^2)\sin k_1(x_2-x)\cos k_1(x_2-x)}{\sin^2 k_1(x_2-x)+n_{12}^2\cos^2 k_1(x_2-x)};\\ \beta'_{1V}&=\frac{k_1n_{12}}{\sin^2 k_1(x_2-x)+n_{12}^2\cos^2 k_1(x_2-x)};\\ \alpha'_{1T}&=\frac{k_1(1-n_{21}^2)\sin k_1(x_2-x)\cos k_1(x_2-x)}{\sin^2 k_1(x_2-x)+n_{21}^2\cos^2 k_1(x_2-x)};\\ \beta'_{1T}&=\frac{k_1n_{21}}{\sin^2 k_1(x_2-x)+n_{21}^2\cos^2 k_1(x_2-x)}.\end{aligned}\right\}\tag{73}$$

Transforming the trigonometric functions to binary arguments, we eventually obtain the unknown coefficients:

$$\alpha'_{1V}=\frac{k_1\cdot\dfrac{W_2^2-W_1^2}{W_2^2+W_1^2}\cdot\sin 2k_1(x_2-x)}{1+\dfrac{-W_2^2+W_1^2}{W_1^2+W_2^2}\cos 2k_1(x_2-x)};\qquad \beta'_{1V}=\frac{2\dfrac{k_1W_1W_2}{W_1^2+W_2^2}}{1+\dfrac{-W_2^2+W_1^2}{W_1^2+W_2^2}\cos 2k_1(x_2-x)};$$

$$\alpha'_{1T}=\frac{k_1\cdot\dfrac{W_1^2-W_2^2}{W_1^2+W_2^2}\cdot\sin 2k_1(x_2-x)}{1+\dfrac{-W_1^2+W_2^2}{W_1^2+W_2^2}\cos 2k_1(x_2-x)};\qquad \beta'_{1T}=\frac{2\dfrac{k_1W_1W_2}{W_1^2+W_2^2}}{1+\dfrac{-W_1^2+W_2^2}{W_1^2+W_2^2}\cos 2k_1(x_2-x)}. \tag{74}$$

In order to determine the differential velocity c', i.e., the phase velocity of the pressure wave or of the velocity wave over an infinitesimally small waveguide section, we make use of the identity [22]:

$$c=\frac{\omega\Delta x}{\Delta\beta}, \tag{75}$$

where $\Delta\beta$ is the phase shift occurring over an element of path Δx. Going to the limit, we obtain

$$c'=\lim_{\Delta x\to 0}\frac{\omega\Delta x}{\Delta\beta}=\frac{\omega}{\beta'}, \tag{76}$$

where c' is the differential (phase) velocity, and β' is the differential phase-shift constant.

We next determine the differential true phase velocities c'_V and c'_T; for this purpose, we substitute β'_{1V} and β'_{1T} into (76) [cf. (73)].

$$\left.\begin{aligned} c'_{1V}&=c_1 n_{21}[\sin^2 k_1(x_2-x)+n_{12}^2\cos k_1(x_2-x)],\\ c'_{1T}&=c_1 n_{12}[\sin^2 k_1(x_2-x)+n_{21}^2\cos k_1(x_2-x)].\end{aligned}\right\} \tag{77}$$

or in terms of trigonometric functions of binary angles (74)

$$\left.\begin{aligned} c'_{1V}&=c_1\frac{W_1^2+W_2^2}{2W_1W_2}\left[1+\frac{W_1^2-W_2^2}{W_1^2+W_2^2}\cos 2k_1(x_2-x)\right];\\ c'_{1T}&=c_1\frac{W_1^2+W_2^2}{2W_1W_2}\left[1-\frac{W_1^2-W_2^2}{W_1^2+W_2^2}\cos 2k_1(x_2-x)\right],\end{aligned}\right\} \tag{78}$$

which characterize the variation in the velocity of propagation from point to point in the first medium, where interference takes place between the incident and the reflected wave, i.e., there is a resultant wave.

According to (78), we plot a graph (Fig. 5), from which we have that the phase velocity of the resultant wave varies from point to point in obedience to a sinusoidal law.

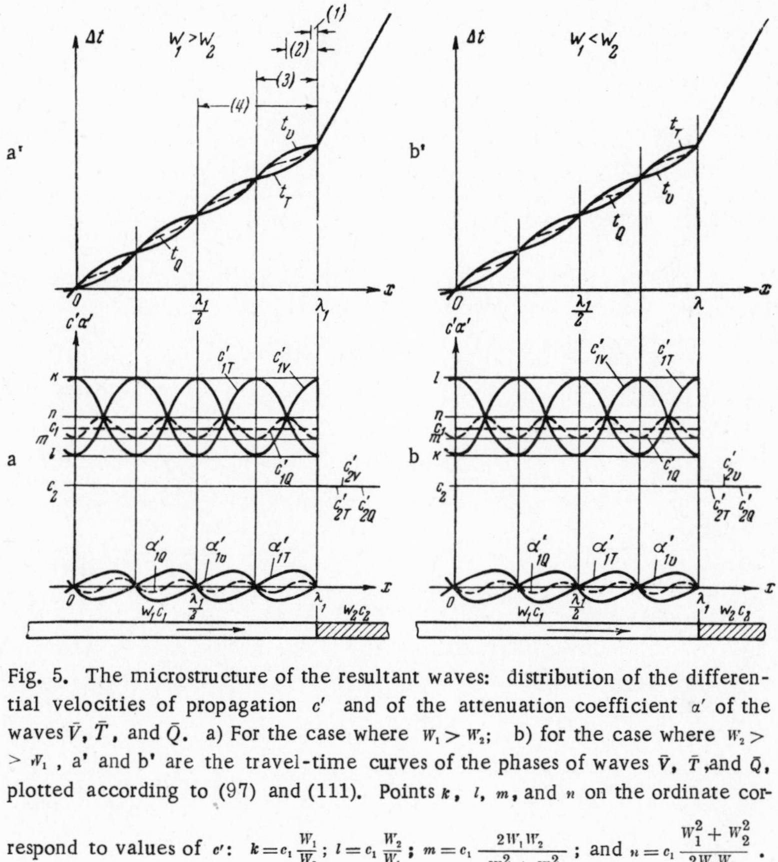

Fig. 5. The microstructure of the resultant waves: distribution of the differential velocities of propagation c' and of the attenuation coefficient α' of the waves $\bar{V}$, $\bar{T}$, and $\bar{Q}$. a) For the case where $W_1 > W_2$; b) for the case where $W_2 > W_1$, a' and b' are the travel-time curves of the phases of waves $\bar{V}$, $\bar{T}$, and $\bar{Q}$, plotted according to (97) and (111). Points k, l, m, and n on the ordinate correspond to values of c': $k = c_1 \frac{W_1}{W_2}$; $l = c_1 \frac{W_2}{W_1}$; $m = c_1 \frac{2W_1W_2}{W_1^2 + W_2^2}$; and $n = c_1 \frac{W_1^2 + W_2^2}{2W_1W_2}$.

The amplitude of the resultant wave [cf. equations for α in (74)] also varies with the distance x according to a periodic law. The period of the variation in the phase velocity c' and the attenuation factor α' of the velocity wave and of the pressure wave, with the distance x, is equal to the half wavelength for that medium, i.e., λ_1.

We now proceed to a determination of the differential propagation constant $\vec{D}_Q$ in the first medium, characterizing the microstructure of the intensity wave. For this, we substitute the values found above for $\vec{D}_{1V}$ and $\vec{D}_{1T}$ (67) into equation (26); after some algebra, we have:

$$\vec{D}_{1Q}=\frac{1}{2}(\vec{D}_{1V}+\vec{D}_{1T})=$$

$$=\frac{\bar{q}_{01}}{2}\cdot\frac{2\,\mathrm{th}\,\bar{q}_{01}(x_2-x)-\mu_{12}[1+\mathrm{th}^2\,\bar{q}_{01}(x_2-x)]}{\mu_{12}\cdot\mathrm{th}\,\bar{q}_{01}(x_2-x)+\frac{1}{2}[1+\mathrm{th}^2\,\bar{q}_{01}(x_2-x)]}=f_Q(x,\,p), \tag{79}$$

where we have, by definition, $\mu_{12}=\frac{W_1^2+W_2^2}{2W_1W_2}=\frac{1}{2}(n_{12}+n_{21})$. We next multiply the numerator and the denominator by $\mathrm{ch}^2\,\bar{q}_{01}(x_2-x)$ and, doubling the angles, we obtain:

$$\vec{D}_{1Q}=\bar{q}_{01}\frac{\mathrm{sh}\,2\bar{q}_{01}(x_2-x)+\mu_{12}\mathrm{ch}\,2\bar{q}_{01}(x_2-x)}{\mu_{12}\,\mathrm{sh}\,2\bar{q}_{01}(x_2-x)+\mathrm{ch}\,2q_{01}(x_2-x)}=f_Q(x,\,p). \tag{80}$$

For steady-state sinusoidal oscillations $(p=i\omega)$, the differential propagation constant of the intensity wave (80) is written in the following manner:

$$\vec{D}_{1Q}=\alpha'_{1Q}+i\beta'_{1Q}=ik_1\frac{i\sin 2k_1(x_2-x)+\mu_{12}\cos 2k_1(x_2-x)}{i\mu_{12}\cdot\sin 2k_1(x_2-x)+\cos 2k_1(x_2-x)}=F_Q(x,\,\omega), \tag{81}$$

where $\alpha'_{1Q}=\frac{1}{2}(\alpha'_{1V}+\alpha'_{1T})$; $\beta'_{1Q}=\frac{1}{2}(\beta'_{1V}+\beta'_{1T})$. Using the dependence of α'_{1Q} on α'_{1V} and α'_{1T} , and that of β'_{1Q} on β'_{1V} and β'_{1T}, or solving for the real and imaginary parts in (81), we obtain the values of the differential attenuation factors α'_{1Q} and the differential phase constant β'_{1Q} for the intensity wave:

$$\alpha'_{1Q}=\frac{k_1\varkappa_{12}^2\sin 2k_1(x_2-x)\cos 2k_1(x_2-x)}{1+\varkappa_{12}^2\sin^2 2k_1(x_2-x)};\qquad \beta'_{1Q}=\frac{k_1\mu_{12}}{1+\varkappa_{12}^2\sin^2 2k_1(x_2-x)}, \tag{82}$$

where we have, by definition:

$$\varkappa_{12}=\frac{W_1^2-W_2^2}{2W_1W_2};\quad \mu_{12}=\frac{W_1^2+W_2^2}{2W_1W_2}\quad k_1=\frac{\omega}{c_1}=\frac{2\pi}{\lambda_1}.$$

Representing equations (82) in terms of functions of twice the angles, we eventually arrive at the unknown coefficients:

$$\alpha'_{1Q}=\frac{k_1\varkappa_{12}\sin 4k_1(x_2-x)}{1+\mu_{12}^2-\varkappa_{12}^2\cos 4k_1(x_2-x)};\qquad \beta'_{1Q}=\frac{2k_1\mu_{12}}{1+\mu_{12}^2-\varkappa_{12}^2\cos 4k_1(x_2-x)}. \tag{83}$$

Making use of the value of β'_{1Q} from (76), we find the differential velocity of the intensity wave in the first medium:

$$c'_{1Q}=\frac{\omega}{\beta'_{1Q}}=c_1\frac{1}{2\mu_{12}}[1+\mu_{12}^2-\varkappa_{12}^2\cos 4k_1(x_2-x)]=f_{Qc}(\omega,\ x). \quad (84)$$

As follows from (83) and (84), the differential coefficients α'_{1Q} and β'_{1Q}, as well as the velocity of the intensity wave c'_{1Q} vary with the distance x [cf. the graphs in Fig. 5, plotted on the basis of (83) and (84)]. The period of the variation with distance x is four times smaller than the wavelength λ_1 in that medium. Graphs are plotted in Fig. 5a for α'_{1V} ; α'_{1T} ; α'_{1Q} ; c'_{1V} ; c'_{1T} and c'_{1Q} for the case where the sinusoidal wave is incident on the interface beyond which a second medium with a smaller wave impedance, i.e., $W_1 > W_2$, is to be found, while in Fig. 5b we have a second medium with a larger wave impedance, i.e., $W_1 < W_2$. For the limiting cases $W_2 \to 0$ and $W_2 \to \infty$ [cf. formulas (78) and (84)] the differential velocities of the velocity waves, pressure waves, and intensity waves at a series of points in the first medium vanish, and those points constitute the conditions for the respective standing waves. At all remaining points in the first medium, the values of the differential propagation velocities tend to infinity, which corresponds to all points between nodes of the waves traveling in phase.

For our subsequent discussion, it is well to note that near the interface ($x \leqslant x_2$), in the case of mismatching of wave impedances of continuous media, the differential velocity of the intensity wave is everywhere (i.e., both at $W_1 > W_2$ and at $W_1 < W_2$) less than the computed velocity c_1 for that medium.

The Integral Propagation Constant

Up to this point, we have been interested in the differential wave characteristics of the medium in which interference is taking place between two oppositely directed waves of differing amplitudes (the interface may constitute a source of oscillations of amplitude and phase which are dependent on the ratios of the wave impedances of the media).

In order to find the integral wave characteristics, i.e., the characteristics defined for a finite segment of path Δx, we next integrate $\vec{D}_{1V}$; $\vec{D}_{1T}$ and $\vec{D}_{1Q}$, availing ourselves of (29) and (30).

According to (29), (30) and (67), the integral propagation constants for the first medium (the integration is performed in the direction of advance of the wave, i.e., along the abscissa, over the interval $x_2 - x_1 = \Delta x$, where x_1 is the instantaneous coordinate varying over the range extending from $-\infty$ to x_2) are:

$$\left.\begin{aligned}
\vec{S}_{1V}(x, p) &= \int_{x_1}^{x_2} \vec{D}_{1V} dx = \int_{x_1}^{x_2} \frac{n_{21} + \text{th}\,\bar{q}_{01}(x_2 - x)}{n_{21} \cdot \text{th}\,\bar{q}_{01}(x_2 - x) + 1} \bar{q}_{01} dx = \\
&= \int_{x_1}^{x_2} \frac{(1 + n_{21})\, e^{\bar{q}_{01}(x_2 - x)} + (n_{21} - 1)\, e^{-\bar{q}_{01}(x_2 - x)}}{(1 + n_{21})\, e^{\bar{q}_{01}(x_2 - x)} + (n_{21} - 1)\, e^{-\bar{q}_{01}(x_2 - x)}} \cdot \bar{q}_{01} \cdot dx, \\
\vec{S}_{1T}(x, p) &\int_{x_1} \vec{D}_{1T} dx = \int_{x_1}^{x_2} \frac{n_{21} \cdot \text{th}\,\bar{q}_{01}(x_2 - x) + 1}{n_{21} + \text{th}\,\bar{q}_{01}(x_2 - x)} q_{01} dx = \\
&= \int_{x_1}^{x_2} \frac{(1 + n_{12})\, e^{\bar{q}_{01}(x_2 - x)} + (n_{12} - 1)\, e^{-\bar{q}(x_2 - x)}}{(1 + n_{12})\, e^{\bar{q}_{01}(x_2 - x)} + (n_{12} - 1)\, e^{-\bar{q}_{01}(x_2 - x)}} \cdot \bar{q}_{01} dx,
\end{aligned}\right\} \quad (85)$$

where the hyperbolic tangents are replaced by the exponential functions, and we define: $n_{12} = \frac{\overline{W}_1}{\overline{W}_2}$; $n_{21} = \frac{\overline{W}_2}{\overline{W}_1}$.

In order to perform the integration, we transform (85). For this purpose, we multiply the numerator and the denominator by $e^{\bar{q}_{01}(x_2 - x)}$ and represent the function in terms of two integrals:

$$\vec{S}_{1V}(x, p) = q_{01} \int_{x_1}^{x_2} \frac{-e^{2\bar{q}_{01}(x_2 - x)} d\,(x_2 - x)}{e^{2\bar{q}_{01}(x_2 - x)} + \frac{1 - n_{21}}{1 + n_{21}}} + q_{01} \int_{x_1}^{x_2} \frac{-\frac{n_{21} - 1}{n_{21} + 1} d\,(x_2 - x)}{e^{2\bar{q}_{01}(x_2 - x)} + \frac{1 - n_{21}}{1 + n_{21}}} \quad (86)$$

(similar to the way in which the equation for the integral propagation constant of the pressure wave $\vec{S}_{1T}$ was obtained). Making use of a table of integrals [23], we obtain:

$$\begin{aligned}
\vec{S}_{1V}(x, p) &= -\left| \frac{1}{2} \ln\left(\frac{1 - n_{21}}{1 + n_{21}} + e^{2\bar{q}_{01}(x_2 - x)}\right)\right|_{x_1}^{x_2} + \frac{1}{2}\left|\left[2\bar{q}_{01}(x_2 - x) - \right.\right. \\
&\left.\left. - \ln\left(\frac{1 - n_{21}}{1 + n_{21}}\right) + e^{2\bar{q}_{01}(x_2 - x)}\right]\right|_{x_1}^{x_2} = -\left| \ln\left(\frac{1 - n_{21}}{1 + n_{21}} + e^{2\bar{q}_{01}(x_2 - x)}\right) - \right. \\
&\left. - \bar{q}_{01}(x_2 - x)\right|_{x_1}^{x_2} = +\left| \ln\left(\frac{1 - n_{21}}{1 + n_{21}} e^{-\bar{q}_{01}(x_2 - x)} + e^{\bar{q}_{01}(x_2 - x)}\right)\right|_{x_1}^{x_2}.
\end{aligned} \quad (87)$$

Substituting the limits of integration, we obtain:

$$\begin{aligned}
\vec{S}_{1V} &= \ln\left(\frac{1 - n_{21}}{1 + n_{21}} e^{-\bar{q}_{01}\Delta x} + e^{\bar{q}_{01}\Delta x}\right) - \ln\left(\frac{2}{1 + n_{21}}\right) = \\
&= \ln\left(\frac{1 - n_{21}}{2} e^{-\bar{q}_{01}\Delta x} + \frac{1 + n_{21}}{2} e^{\bar{q}_{01}\Delta x}\right),
\end{aligned} \quad (88)$$

where we define $\Delta x = x_2 - x_1$. The value found for $\vec{S}_{1V}$ constitutes the integral propagation constant for the velocity wave over the interval $\Delta x = x_2 - x_1$, which joins the interface on its right edge.

Performing a similar integration for the pressure wave, we obtain the value of $\vec{S}_{1T}$ over the same interval $\Delta x = x_2 - x_1$:

$$\vec{S}_{1T} = \ln\left(\frac{1 - n_{12}}{2} e^{-\bar{q}_{01}\Delta x} + \frac{1 + n_{12}}{2} e^{\bar{q}_{01}\Delta x}\right). \tag{89}$$

From (88) and (89), we have that in the case of matched wave impedances, i.e., $n_{12} = n_{21} = 1$, the integral propagation constants become equal for any interval Δx:

$$\vec{S}_{1V} = \vec{S}_{1T} = \Delta x \cdot \bar{q}_{01}. \tag{90}$$

For steady-state sinusoidal oscillations $\left(\bar{q}_{01} = \frac{i\omega}{c_1} = ik_1\right)$, (88) and (89) take on the following form:

$$\left.\begin{aligned} \vec{S}_{1V}(x, \omega) &= \ln\left(\frac{1 - n_{21}}{2} e^{-ik_1\Delta x} + \frac{1 + n_{21}}{2} e^{ik_1\Delta x}\right); \\ \vec{S}_{1T}(x, \omega) &= \ln\left(\frac{1 - n_{12}}{2} e^{-ik_1\Delta x} + \frac{1 + n_{12}}{2} e^{ik_1\Delta x}\right). \end{aligned}\right\} \tag{91}$$

We make use of Euler's formula for transforming exponential complex functions into trigonometric functions. With this, we arrive at:

$$\begin{aligned} \vec{S}_{1V}(x, \omega) &= \ln(\cos k_1 \Delta x + i n_{21} \sin k_1 \Delta x); \\ \vec{S}_{1T}(x, \omega) &= \ln(\cos k_1 \Delta x + i n_{12} \sin k_1 \Delta x). \end{aligned} \tag{92}$$

Separating the real and imaginary parts, we obtain:

$$\left.\begin{aligned} \vec{S}_{1V} &= \ln\sqrt{\cos^2 k_1 \Delta x + n_{21}^2 \sin^2 k_1 \Delta x} + i \operatorname{arctg}(n_{21} \operatorname{tg} k_1 \Delta x), \\ \vec{S}_{1T} &= \ln\sqrt{\cos^2 k_1 \Delta x + n_{12}^2 \sin^2 k_1 \Delta x} + i \operatorname{arctg}(n_{12} \operatorname{tg} k_1 \Delta x). \end{aligned}\right\} \tag{93}$$

From this, we now find the integral attenuation and phase-shift constants over the baseline $\Delta x = x_2 - x_1$ for a velocity wave and a pressure wave[1] [according to (2)]:

[1] These constants may be obtained directly by taking the integration of the differential attenuation constant α' and phase constant β' (74), as is done here.

$$\left.\begin{aligned}
\alpha_{1V} &= \ln\sqrt{\cos^2 k_1\,\Delta x + \frac{W_2^2}{W_1^2}\sin^2 k_1\Delta x} = \ln\left(\frac{V_{x1}}{V_{x2}}\right);\\
\beta_{1V} &= \operatorname{arctg}\left(\frac{W_2}{W_1}\operatorname{tg} k_1\Delta x\right);\\
\alpha_{1T} &= \ln\sqrt{\cos^2 k_1\Delta x + \frac{W_1^2}{W_2^2}\sin^2 k_1\Delta x} = \ln\left(\frac{T_{x1}}{T_{x2}}\right);\\
\beta_{1T} &= \operatorname{arctg}\left(\frac{W_1}{W_2}\operatorname{tg} k_1\Delta x\right),
\end{aligned}\right\} \tag{94a}$$

where V_{x_1} and T_{x_1} are the amplitudes of the oscillation of the velocity and pressure at the point x_1 (cf. Fig. 3), and V_{x_2} and T_{x_2} are the same, at point x_2. From (94a), we find the law governing variations of the amplitudes of V and T in the first medium, as a function of the distance x:

$$\left.\begin{aligned}
\frac{V_{x_1}}{V_{x_2}} &= \sqrt{\cos^2 k_1\Delta x + \frac{W_2^2}{W_1^2}\sin^2 k_1\Delta x} = f_V(x_1\omega),\\
\frac{T_{x_1}}{T_{x_2}} &= \sqrt{\cos^2 k_1\Delta x + \frac{W_1^2}{W_2^2}\sin^2 k_1\Delta x} = f_T(x_1\omega).
\end{aligned}\right\} \tag{94b}$$

To find the equation for the travel-time curve of the phases of the oscillations, we make use of (75), in which the velocity of propagation is expressed in terms of the phase constant:

$$c_S = \frac{\Delta x\cdot\omega}{\beta} = \frac{\Delta x}{\frac{\beta}{\omega}} = \frac{x_2 - x_1}{t_1 - t}, \tag{95}$$

where $\Delta x = (x_2 - x_1)$ is the interval over which the velocity c is being determined, and $\frac{\beta}{\omega} = (t_1 - t)$ is the time required for the phase of the wave to propagate, for some given interval. Assuming x_1 in (95) to be a variable quantity, we obtain the function:

$$\Delta t = t_1 - t = \frac{\beta}{\omega} = f_T(x,\omega), \tag{96}$$

which constitutes the travel-time curve of the phase of the wave. Substituting here the values of the phase-shift constants (94a), we find the equation for the travel-time curves of the velocity and pressure waves in the first medium:

$$\left.\begin{aligned}
\Delta t_{1V} &= \frac{1}{\omega}\operatorname{arctg}\left[\frac{W_2}{W_1}\operatorname{tg} k_1(x_2 - x_1)\right] = t_V(x,\omega),\\
\Delta t_{1T} &= \frac{1}{\omega}\operatorname{arctg}\left[\frac{W_1}{W_2}\operatorname{tg} k_1(x_2 - x_1)\right] = t_T(x,\omega),
\end{aligned}\right\} \tag{97}$$

according to which phase travel-time curves are plotted in Fig. 5a' and 5b' for velocity waves (t_V) and for pressure waves (t_T).

With the aim of clarifying the physical content of the formulas obtained, seismograms are reproduced in Fig. 6 for one type of

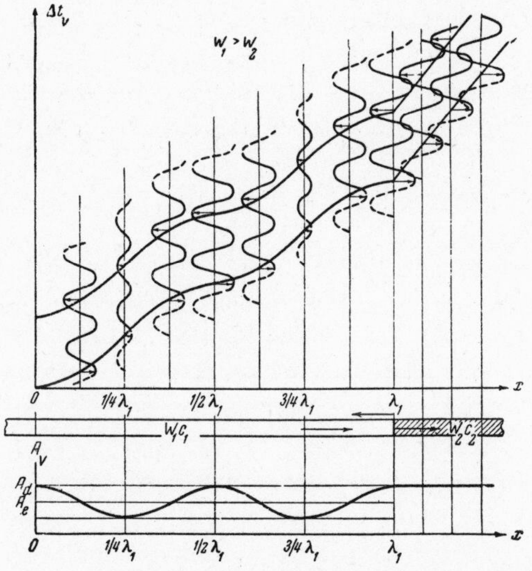

Fig. 6. Seismograms and graphs of the amplitudes $A_V = f(x)$ of the resultant velocity wave for the case where $W_1 > W_2$. On the amplitude graph A_e is the amplitude of the incident wave and A_d is the amplitude of the transmitted wave.

sinusoidal wave, the resultant velocity wave in the first medium and a homogeneous wave in the second medium, as well as a graph of the amplitudes A_V, plotted according to (94b). The graphs of pressure waves may be presented in a manner similar to Fig. 6.

From the graph in Fig. 5 and 6, we have that the resultant velocity and pressure waves in the first medium are characterized by the following features:

1) the phase travel-time curves have a form different from a straight line, whereby the tangents to the corresponding curves, for two arbitrarily chosen phases at the same point in the medium, remain parallel;

2) the amplitude of the wave varies with the distance x according to the law expressed in (94b), and has a period equal to half the wavelength in that medium, i.e., $\lambda_1/2$.

In the limiting case, where the wave impedance of the second medium $W_2 \to 0$, then, in the first medium, as we know, standing waves will exist, while, e.g., for a velocity wave, the phase travel-time curve in Fig. 6 degenerates to segments of horizontal straight lines of length equal to half the wavelength λ_1, i.e., over those segments we shall have phased oscillations of discrete points of the medium, and the amplitude of the oscillations will vary with the distance x according to the law $\frac{V_{x_1}}{V_{x_2}} = \cos(k_1 \Delta x)$.

We now determine, finally, the integral phase velocities and functions of frequency ω over an arbitrary, but constant, baseline $\Delta x_{31} = x_3 - x_1$ (cf. Fig. 3), including the interface between elastic media. For this purpose, having recourse to (95) and equating the phase shift β to the sum of the phase shifts in the first medium, β_1 , and in the second medium, β_2, we find the integral phase velocities of velocity and pressure waves over the baseline Δx_{31}:

$$\left.\begin{aligned} c_{SV}(\omega) &= \frac{\Delta x_{31}}{\frac{1}{\omega}\left[\pi \cdot n + \operatorname{arctg}\left(\frac{W_2}{W_1}\operatorname{tg}\frac{\omega \cdot \Delta x_{21}}{c_1}\right)\right] + \frac{\Delta x_{32}}{c_2}}, \\ c_{ST}(\omega) &= \frac{\Delta x_{31}}{\frac{1}{\omega}\left[\pi \cdot n + \operatorname{arctg}\left(\frac{W_1}{W_2}\operatorname{tg}\frac{\omega \cdot \Delta x_{21}}{c_1}\right)\right] + \frac{\Delta x_{32}}{c_2}}, \end{aligned}\right\} \tag{98}$$

where $n = 1, 2, 3, \ldots$ as a function of the number of half wavelengths accomodated in medium *1*. These formulas indicate the dependence of the phase velocity of V and T waves on the frequency, even in the case of a single interface between media.

Since the amplitudes of the waves, V_{x_2} and T_{x_2} , in the second medium are independent of x, the equations for the amplitudes over the baseline Δx_{31} may be rewritten to conform to (94b), as follows:

$$\left.\begin{aligned} \frac{V_{x_1}}{V_{x_2}} &= \sqrt{\cos^2\frac{\omega \Delta x_{21}}{c_1} + \frac{W_2^2}{W_1^2}\sin^2\frac{\omega \cdot \Delta x_{21}}{c_1}} = F_V(\omega), \\ \frac{T_{x_1}}{T_{x_3}} &= \sqrt{\cos^2\frac{\omega \Delta x_{21}}{c_1} + \frac{W_1^2}{W_2^2}\sin^2\frac{\omega \cdot \Delta x_{21}}{c_1}} = F_T(\omega). \end{aligned}\right\} \tag{99}$$

In Fig. 7, according to (98) and (99), graphs are plotted for the velocities c_{SV}; c_{ST}, and also for the amplitude ratios $\frac{V_{x_1}}{V_{x_3}}$; $\frac{T_{x_1}}{T_{x_3}}$ as functions of the frequency ω, assuming $W_1=3W_2$; $\frac{\Delta x_{21}}{c_2}=\frac{\Delta x_{23}}{c_1}$. For purposes of comparison, the velocity of propagation c_{av} computed on the basis of the formula for average velocities in geometric seismics is plotted on the same graph:

$$c_{\mathrm{av}}=\frac{\Delta x_{31}}{\frac{\Delta x_{21}}{c_1}+\frac{\Delta x_{32}}{c_2}}. \tag{100}$$

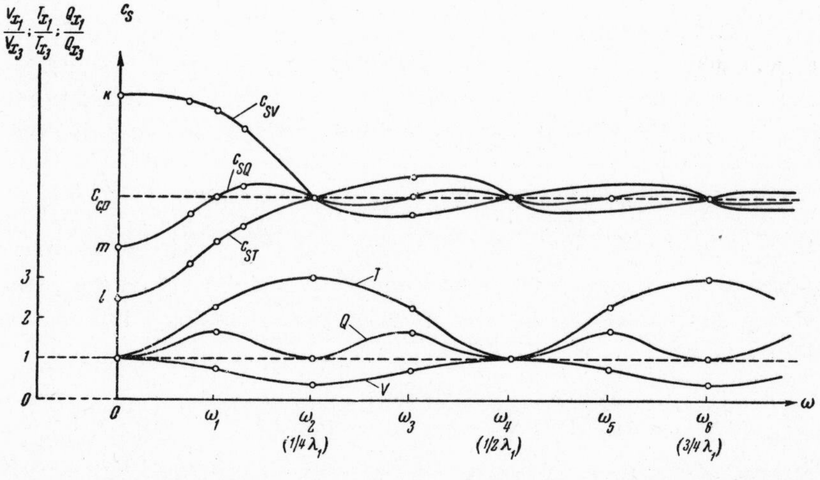

Fig. 7. Macrostructure of the waves. Dispersion of the phase velocities of propagation, and attenuation of $\bar{V}$, $\bar{T}$, and $\bar{Q}$ waves over the baseline $x_3 - x_1$ (cf. Fig. 3), for the case of a single interface. Assumed: $W_1=3W_2$; $\frac{\Delta x_{12}}{c_2}=\frac{\Delta x_{23}}{c_1}$. Points k, l, and m on the ordinate correspond to the following values of the integral velocity c_S:

$$k=c_{\mathrm{av}}\frac{2}{1+n_{21}};\quad l=c_{\mathrm{av}}\frac{2}{1+n_{12}};\quad m=c_{\mathrm{av}}\frac{2}{1+\mu_{12}}.$$

We have from the graph that the dispersion of the phase velocities of the sinusoidal waves V and T over a baseline including the interface is manifested essentially for the lower frequencies.

In the case of intermediate values of the frequency ω, a periodicity is observed in the variation of the phase velocities. For very high frequencies, the phase velocities of the $\bar{V}$ and $\bar{T}$ waves practically coincide with the velocity c_{av}, computed on the basis of the formula for average velocities.

The "decay" of the amplitudes of V and T waves with variation in frequency shows periodic behavior in the particular case ($W_1 = 3W_2$) dealt with in the second medium, the amplitudes of the T wave being always greater (of the V wave always less) than or equal to the amplitude of the resultant wave in the first medium.

It is easily appreciated [cf. (98) and (99)] that, for the reverse relationship between the wave impedances, other conditions being equal:

$$W_2 = 3W_1; \quad \frac{\Delta x_{21}}{c_2} = \frac{\Delta x_{23}}{c_1}, \tag{101}$$

the graphs (cf. Fig. 7) of the integral velocities and of the amplitude ratios for the V and T waves vary only in position. The graphs for the intensity wave Q show no change, as will become clear from the discussion.

The cases discussed involving the behavior of the integral velocities c_S and the coefficients determining the conditions of propagation of the resultant wave will be of aid to us in the further discussion in understanding the wave pattern appearing in layered media.

For a complete clarification of the wave process taking place in the first medium (Fig. 3), we determine the integral propagation constant of the intensity wave. For the case where the oscillations are of arbitrary nature, and are specified in the waveguide, we obtained the following propagation constant [cf. (80)].

$$\vec{D}_{1Q} = \bar{q}_{01} \frac{\text{sh}\, 2\bar{q}_{01}(x_2 - x) + \mu_{12}\,\text{ch}\, 2\bar{q}_{01}(x_2 - x)}{\mu_{12}\,\text{sh}\, 2\bar{q}_{01}(x_2 - x) + \text{ch}\, 2\bar{q}_{01}(x_2 - x)} \bigg|_{-\infty \leqslant x \leqslant x_2} = f_Q(x, p). \tag{102}$$

The integral propagation constant $\vec{S}_{1Q}$ over the baseline $\Delta x = x_2 - x_1$ is determined by the integral:

$$\vec{S}_{1Q} = \int_{x_1}^{x_2} \vec{D}_{1Q} dx = \bar{q}_{01} \int_{x_1}^{x_2} \frac{\text{sh}\, 2\bar{q}_{01}(x_2 - x) + \mu_{12}\,\text{ch}\, 2\bar{q}_{01}(x_2 - x)}{\mu_{12}\,\text{sh}\, 2\bar{q}_{01}(x_2 - x) + \text{ch}\, 2\bar{q}_{01}(x_2 - x)}\, dx. \tag{103}$$

Let us now evaluate the integral. For this purpose, we divide the numerator and the denominator by $\text{ch}\, 2\bar{q}_{01}(x_2 - x)$:

$$\vec{S}_{1Q}=\bar{q}_{01}\int_{x_1}^{x_2}\frac{\operatorname{th}2\bar{q}_{01}(x_2-x_1)+\mu_{12}}{\mu_{12}\operatorname{th}2\bar{q}_{01}(x_2-x)+1}\,dx. \tag{104}$$

In connection with the fact that the general form of the integral coincides with the integral (85), the solution of which is determined by (88), we write the result as:

$$\vec{S}_{1Q}=\frac{1}{2}\ln\left(\frac{1-\mu_{12}}{2}e^{-2\bar{q}_{01}\Delta x}+\frac{1+\mu_{12}}{2}e^{2\bar{q}_{01}\Delta x}\right). \tag{105}$$

For steady-state oscillations, $\bar{q}_{01}=i\frac{\omega}{c_1}=ik_1$; then the integral propagation constant assumes the form:

$$\vec{S}_{1Q}=\frac{1}{2}\ln\left(\frac{1-\mu_{12}}{2}e^{-i2k_1\Delta x}+\frac{1+\mu_{12}}{2}e^{i2k_1\Delta x}\right). \tag{106}$$

Proceeding, with the aid of the Eulerian formulas, to the trigonometric formulas, and separating real and imaginary parts, we obtain:

$$\vec{S}_{1Q}=\ln\sqrt[4]{\cos^2 2k_1\Delta x+\mu_{12}^2\sin^2 k_1\Delta x}+i\,\frac{1}{2}\operatorname{arctg}\left[\mu_{12}\operatorname{tg}(2k_1\Delta x)\right]=$$

$$=\alpha_{1Q}+i\beta_{1Q}, \tag{107}$$

or

$$\alpha_{1Q}=\ln\sqrt[4]{\cos^2 2k_1\Delta x+\mu_{12}^2\sin^2 k_1\Delta x};\quad \beta_{1Q}=\frac{1}{2}\operatorname{arctg}\left[\mu_{12}\operatorname{tg}(2k_1\Delta x)\right], \tag{108}$$

where α_{1Q} is the integral attenuation constant, and β_{1Q} is the integral phase constant of the intensity wave over the baseline Δx; $\mu_{12}=\frac{W_1^2+W_2^2}{2W_1W_2}$.

After obtaining the integral constants α_{1Q} and β_{1Q}, we are in a position to find, according to (95), the integral phase velocity of the intensity wave over the baseline Δx_{31} (cf. Fig. 3):

$$c_{SQ}=\frac{\Delta x_{31}}{\frac{1}{2\omega}\left[\pi n+\operatorname{arctg}\left(\frac{W_1^2+W_2^2}{2W_1W_2}\operatorname{tg}2\frac{\omega\Delta x_{21}}{c_1}\right)\right]+\frac{\Delta x_{32}}{c_2}}, \tag{109}$$

and also the amplitude ratio of the intensity wave:

$$\frac{Q_{x_1}}{Q_{x_3}}=\sqrt{\cos^2\frac{2\omega\cdot\Delta x_{21}}{c_1}+\left(\frac{W_1^2+W_2^2}{2W_1W_2}\right)^2\sin^2\frac{2\omega\cdot\Delta x_{21}}{c_1}}. \tag{110}$$

In Fig. 7, according to (109) and (110), graphs are plotted for the velocity c_{SQ} and the amplitude ratio $\frac{Q_{x_1}}{Q_{x_3}}$ for the intensity wave in the case $W_1=3W_2$ and $\frac{\Delta x_{21}}{c_1}=\frac{\Delta x_{32}}{c_2}$.

It is characteristic of intensity waves [cf. (109) and (110)] that the variation in the ratio of the wave impedances to yield the reciprocal case, i.e., in our case $W_2=3W_1$, is without effect on the position and slope of curves c_{SQ} and $\frac{Q_{x_1}}{Q_{x_3}}$.

The equation of the phase locus of the intensity wave is obtained by substitution of the expression for β_{1Q} from (108) into (96):

$$\Delta t=\frac{\operatorname{arctg}(\mu_{12}\operatorname{tg}2k_1\Delta x)}{2\omega}. \qquad (111)$$

In Fig. 5 [according to (111)], graphs are plotted for the phase loci of the intensity wave (t_Q).

In conclusion, we determine the integral propagation constants over the baseline $\Delta x_{31}=x_3-x_1$ (Fig. 3) in the general form, which may be represented in the form:

$$\Delta x_{31}=(x_3-x_2)+(x_2-x_1)=\Delta x_{32}+\Delta x_{21}. \qquad (112)$$

Since the incident wave propagates from left to right, the input impedance for the waves in the second medium is at any point equal to the wave impedance of that medium, and, accordingly:

$$\vec{S}_{2V}=\vec{S}_{2T}=\vec{S}_{2Q}=\Delta x_{32}\cdot\bar{q}_{02}. \qquad (113)$$

Since the integral constants for the first medium have been determined [cf. (91) and (105)], we may write for the baseline Δx_{31}:

$$\left.\begin{aligned}
\vec{S}_V(\Delta x_{31})&=\vec{S}_{1V}(\Delta x_{12})+\vec{S}_{2V}(\Delta x_{32})=\ln\left(\frac{1-n_{21}}{2}e^{-\bar{q}_{01}\Delta x_{21}}+\right.\\
&\qquad\left.+\frac{1+n_{21}}{2}e^{\bar{q}_{01}\Delta x_{21}}\right)+\Delta x_{32}\bar{q}_{02};\\
\vec{S}_T(\Delta x_{31})&=\vec{S}_{1T}(\Delta x_{12})+\vec{S}_{2T}(\Delta x_{32})=\ln\left(\frac{1-n_{12}}{2}e^{-\bar{q}_{01}\Delta x_{21}}+\right.\\
&\qquad\left.+\frac{1+n_{12}}{2}e^{\bar{q}_{01}\Delta x_{21}}\right)+\Delta x_{32}\bar{q}_{02};\\
\vec{S}_Q(\Delta x_{31})&=\vec{S}_{1Q}(\Delta x_{12})+\vec{S}_{2Q}(\Delta x_{32})=\frac{1}{2}\ln\left(\frac{1-\mu_{12}}{2}e^{-2\bar{q}_{01}\Delta x_{21}}+\right.\\
&\qquad\left.+\frac{1+\mu_{12}}{2}e^{2\bar{q}_{01}\Delta x_{21}}\right)+\Delta x_{32}\bar{q}_{02}.
\end{aligned}\right\} \qquad (114)$$

The integral propagation constants, according to (11) and (19), are determined as

$$\vec{S}_V(\Delta x_{31}) = \ln\frac{\bar{V}_1}{\bar{V}_2}; \quad \vec{S}_T(\Delta x_{31}) = \ln\frac{\bar{T}_1}{\bar{T}_2}; \quad \vec{S}_Q(\Delta x_{31}) = \ln\frac{\bar{Q}_1}{\bar{Q}_2}; \tag{115}$$

where, respectively, $\bar{V}_1$, $\bar{T}_1$ and $\bar{Q}_1 = \bar{V}_1 \cdot \bar{T}_1$ are the values of the velocity, pressure, and intensity at the input of the waveguide section treated, and $\bar{V}_2$, $\bar{T}_2$ and $\bar{Q}_2 = \bar{V}_2 \cdot \bar{T}_2$ are the same at the section output. The values of $\bar{V}_1$, $\bar{T}_1$, $\bar{Q}_1$ are, as we know [2], the vector sum of the oscillations of the incident (subscript l) and of the reflected (index r) waves:

$$\left.\begin{aligned} \bar{V}_1 &= \bar{V}_{1l} + \bar{V}_{1r}; \\ \bar{T}_1 &= \bar{T}_{1l} + \bar{T}_{1r}; \\ \bar{Q}_1 &= \bar{Q}_{1l} + \bar{Q}_{1r}. \end{aligned}\right\} \tag{116}$$

At the waveguide section output (Δx_{31}), $\bar{V}_2$, $\bar{T}_2$ and $\bar{Q}_2$ are the magnitudes of the oscillations in the transmitted waves (which shall be designated by the subscript d). Formulas (115) are presented in terms of the complex reflection coefficient $\bar{R}$ and the complex transmission coefficient $\bar{\Pi}$, using (116):

$$\left.\begin{aligned} \vec{S}_V(\Delta x_{31}) &= \ln\left(\frac{\bar{V}_{1l} + \bar{V}_{1r}}{\bar{V}_{2d}}\right) = \ln\left[\frac{1}{\bar{\Pi}_V}(\bar{R}_V + 1)\right]; \\ \vec{S}_T(\Delta x_{31}) &= \ln\left(\frac{\bar{T}_{1l} + \bar{T}_{1r}}{\bar{T}_{2d}}\right) = \ln\left[\frac{1}{\bar{\Pi}_T}(\bar{R}_T + 1)\right]; \\ \vec{S}_Q(\Delta x_{31}) &= \frac{1}{2}\ln\left(\frac{\bar{Q}_{1l} + \bar{Q}_{1r}}{\bar{Q}_{2d}}\right) = \frac{1}{2}\ln\left[\frac{1}{\bar{\Pi}_Q}(\bar{R}_Q + 1)\right]. \end{aligned}\right\} \tag{117}$$

Substituting, in the left-hand member of the equations so obtained, their values in (114) and eliminating logarithmic expressions, we obtain, after some algebra:

$$\left.\begin{aligned} \frac{1}{\bar{\Pi}_V}(\bar{R}_V + 1) &= \left(\frac{1 - n_{21}}{1 + n_{21}} \cdot e^{-2\bar{q}_{01}\Delta x_{21}} + 1\right)\left(\frac{1 + n_{21}}{2}\right)\exp(\bar{q}_{01}\Delta x_{21} + \bar{q}_{02}\Delta x_{32}); \\ \frac{1}{\bar{\Pi}_T}(\bar{R}_T + 1) &= \left(\frac{1 - n_{12}}{1 + n_{12}} \cdot e^{-2\bar{q}_{01}\Delta x_{21}} + 1\right)\left(\frac{1 + n_{12}}{2}\right)\exp(\bar{q}_{01}\Delta x_{21} + \bar{q}_{02}\Delta x_{32}); \\ \frac{1}{\bar{\Pi}_Q}(\bar{R}_Q + 1) &= \left(\frac{1 - \mu_{12}}{1 + \mu_{12}} \cdot e^{-4\bar{q}_{01}\Delta x_{21}} + 1\right)\left(\frac{1 + \mu_{12}}{2}\right)\exp(2\bar{q}_{01}\Delta x_{21} + 2\bar{q}_{02}\Delta x_{32}). \end{aligned}\right\} \tag{118}$$

Each of those equations breaks down in two further equations:

$$\left.\begin{aligned}
\overline{R}_V &= \frac{1-n_{21}}{1+n_{21}}\cdot e^{-2\bar{q}_{01}\Delta x_{21}}; \quad \overline{\Pi}_V = \frac{2}{1+n_{21}}\exp\left(-\bar{q}_{01}\Delta x_{21}-\bar{q}_{02}\Delta x_{32}\right);\\
\overline{R}_T &= \frac{1-n_{12}}{1+n_{12}}\cdot e^{-2\bar{q}_{01}\Delta x_{21}}; \quad \overline{\Pi}_T = \frac{2}{1+n_{12}}\exp\left(-\bar{q}_{01}\Delta x_{21}-\bar{q}_{02}\Delta x_{32}\right);\\
\overline{R}_Q &= \frac{1-\mu_{12}}{1+\mu_{12}}\cdot e^{-4\bar{q}_{01}\Delta x_{21}}; \quad \overline{\Pi}_Q = \frac{2}{1+\mu_{12}}\exp\left(-2\bar{q}_{01}\Delta x_{21}-2\bar{q}_{02}\Delta x_{32}\right).
\end{aligned}\right\} \quad (119)$$

In the steady-state mode of oscillations $\left(\bar{q}_0 = \frac{i\omega}{c}\right)$, the absolute values of those equations yield the generally familiar reflection and transmission coefficients of the velocity, pressure, and intensity waves for the case of a single interface (substituting the values of n_{12}; n_{21}; μ_{12});

$$\left.\begin{aligned}
R_V &= \frac{W_1-W_2}{W_1+W_2}; \quad \Pi_V = \frac{2W_1}{W_1+W_2};\\
R_T &= -\frac{W_1-W_2}{W_1+W_2}; \quad \Pi_T = \frac{2W_2}{W_1+W_2};\\
R_Q &= -\left(\frac{W_1-W_2}{W_1+W_2}\right)^2; \quad \Pi_Q = \frac{4W_1W_2}{(W_1+W_2)^2}.
\end{aligned}\right\} \quad (120)$$

The arguments in (119) characterize the phase shift for the corresponding waves between points x_1 and x_3, although the arguments for the intensity waves yield the doubled value of the phase shift referred to.

SECTION FOUR

INCIDENCE OF A PLANE WAVE NORMAL TO A LAYER LOCATED BETWEEN TWO ELASTIC HALF-SPACES

Let us now investigate the micro- and macrostructure of waves traversing a nonhomogeneous medium (Fig. 8), assuming the directions of propagation of the resultant wave and of the x axis to be from left to right. Considering a steady-state mode of oscillations ($p = i\omega$) in the medium (Fig. 8), we find that the input terminal impedances $\vec{Z}_1$ in medium *1* will be equal to the wave impedance

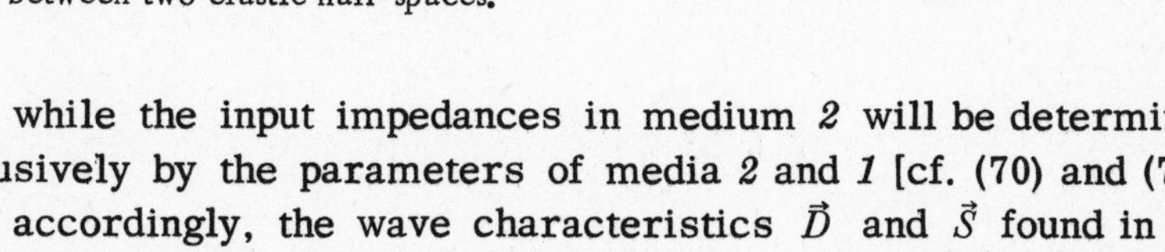

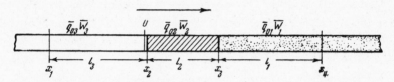

Fig. 8. Acoustical waveguide arbitrarily cut out normal to a layer situated between two elastic half-spaces.

$\bar{W}_1$, while the input impedances in medium *2* will be determined exclusively by the parameters of media *2* and *1* [cf. (70) and (79)] and, accordingly, the wave characteristics $\vec{D}$ and $\vec{S}$ found in the preceding section will be fully applicable to the media *1* and *2* in Fig. 8 (however, with subscripts *1* and *2* interchanged, in view of the opposite arrangement of the media). In other words, if the waveguide section appearing in Fig. 3 on the left, extending from $x = x_1$, were to be replaced by another waveguide, with parameters $\bar{W}_3$ and $\bar{q}_3$, then, in the steady-state mode of oscillations, the microstructure of the waves in the waveguide would not change for the range of values of x extending from x_1 to $+\infty$. The circumstance is to be explained by the fact that a sinusoidal wave emerging from medium *3* adds continuously in the second medium to the wave reflected from the interface at x_2 (cf. Fig. 8), to form a total wave which is unidirectional in motion (and also sinusoidal). This total wave in medium *2* naturally effects no change in the distribution of the input impedances in the second medium, nor accordingly in the values of $\vec{D}_{2V}$, $\vec{D}_{2T}$, $\vec{D}_{2Q}$, which are due solely to the relationships obtaining between the wave impedances at the interface x_3, and to the distance of the interface from the point where the differential propagation constants are determined.

The problem becomes much more complicated when we consider nonsteady-state oscillations with the source of the oscillations placed in the second medium. In that case, the wave phenomena over a certain baseline in the second medium (Fig. 8) are essentially dependent on the presence of the interface at x_2, which must be taken into account, for example, by the use of specially formulated conditions or by means of an additional determination of $\overleftarrow{D}$ and $\overleftarrow{S}$ for the reverse direction. It is suggested below that the source always be found in the third medium and outside the region of the waveguide under consideration.

Differential Propagation Constants

We now determine $\vec{D}_3$ in the third medium (Fig. 8). For this purpose, it is necessary first of all to find the input impedance in medium *3* $[\vec{Z}_3(x)]$. The input impedance $\vec{Z}_3(x)$ is determined, according to formulas (36) to (40):

$$\vec{Z}_3(x) = \overline{W}_3 \frac{\vec{Z}_2(x_2) + \overline{W}_3 \operatorname{th} \bar{q}_{03}(x_2 - x)}{\vec{Z}_2(x_2) \cdot \operatorname{th} \bar{q}_{03}(x_2 - x) + \overline{W}_3} \Bigg|_{-\infty < x < x_2}, \tag{121}$$

where

$$\vec{Z}_2(x_2) = \overline{W}_2 \frac{\overline{W}_1 + W_2 \operatorname{th} \bar{q}_{02} l_2}{W_1 \cdot \operatorname{th} \bar{q}_{02} l_2 + \overline{W}_2}. \tag{122}$$

After substituting $\vec{Z}_2(x_2)$ into equation $\vec{Z}_3(x)$, we obtain

$$\vec{Z}_3(x) = \overline{W}_3 \frac{\overline{W}_1 \overline{W}_2 + \overline{W}_2^2 \operatorname{th} \bar{q}_{02} l_2 + \overline{W}_1 \overline{W}_3 \operatorname{th} \bar{q}_{03}(x_2 - x) \operatorname{th} \bar{q}_{02} l_2 + \overline{W}_2 \overline{W}_3 \operatorname{th} \bar{q}_{03}(x_2 - x)}{\overline{W}_1 W_2 \operatorname{th} \bar{q}_{03}(x_2 - x) + W_2^2 \operatorname{th} \bar{q}_{02} l_2 \operatorname{th} \bar{q}_{03}(x_2 - x) + \overline{W}_1 \overline{W}_3 \operatorname{th} \bar{q}_{02} l_2 + \overline{W}_2 \overline{W}_3}. \tag{123}$$

With $\vec{Z}_3(x)$ known, we may at the same time fully determine the differential propagation constants of the velocity and pressure waves in the third medium:

$$\vec{D}_{3V}(x)=\bar{q}_{03}\frac{\vec{Z}_3(x)}{\overline{W}_3};\quad \vec{D}_{3T}(x)=\bar{q}_{03}\frac{\overline{W}_3}{\vec{Z}_3(x)}, \tag{124}$$

which enable us to investigate transient wave processes taking place in the medium under study.

In the case of steady-state oscillations and absence of resistive losses in media *1*, *2* and *3*, $\vec{D}_{3V}(x)$ and $\vec{D}_{3T}(x)$ assume the following form $\left(\bar{q}_{03}=i\frac{\omega}{c_3}=ik_3\ ;\ \bar{q}_{02}=i\frac{\omega}{c_2}=ik_2\right)$:

$$\left.\begin{aligned}\vec{D}_{3V}&=k_3\frac{-A_1+iA_2}{B_1+iB_2};\\ \vec{D}_{3T}&=k_3\frac{-B_2+iB_1}{A_2+iA_1},\end{aligned}\right\} \tag{125}$$

where we have defined:

$$\left.\begin{aligned}&A_1=W_2^2\,\mathrm{tg}\,k_2l_2+W_2W_3\,\mathrm{tg}\,k_3(x_2-x);\ A_2=W_1W_2-W_1W_3\,\mathrm{tg}\,k_3(x_2-x)\,\mathrm{tg}\,k_2l_2;\\ &B=W_2W_3-W_2^2\,\mathrm{tg}\,k_3(x_2-x)\,\mathrm{tg}\,k_2l_2;\ B_2=W_1W_2\,\mathrm{tg}\,k_3(x_2-x)+W_1W_3\,\mathrm{tg}\,k_2l_2.\end{aligned}\right\} \tag{126}$$

Eliminating the imaginary part in the numerator and separating imaginary and real parts, we obtain:

$$\left.\begin{aligned}\vec{D}_{3V}&=k_3\frac{-A_1B_1+A_2B_2}{B_1^2+B_2^2}+ik_3\frac{A_2B_1+A_1B_2}{B_1^2+B_2^2}=\alpha'_{3V}+i\beta'_{3V};\\ \vec{D}_{3T}&=k_3\frac{-A_2B_2+A_1B_1}{A_1^2+A_2^2}+ik_3\frac{A_2B_1+A_1B_2}{A_1^2+A_2^2}=\alpha'_{3T}+i\beta'_{3T}.\end{aligned}\right\} \tag{127}$$

From this, after substituting the values defined in (126) and after cumbersome transformations, we find the differential attenuation and phase constants for the velocity wave:

$$\alpha'_{3V}=-k_3\times$$

$$\times\frac{\eta_{32}\sin 2k_3(x_2-x)+\eta_{21}\sin 2k_3(x_2-x)\cos k_2l_2+\frac{\eta_{31}}{\mu_{32}}\sin 2k_2l_2\cos 2k_3(x_2-x)}{1+\eta_{32}\cos 2k_3(x_2-x)+[\eta_{32}+\cos 2k_3(x_2-x)]\,\eta_{21}\cos 2k_2l_2-\frac{\eta_{21}}{\mu_{32}}\sin 2k_3(x_2-x)\sin 2k_2l_2};$$

$$\beta'_{3V}=\frac{k_3}{\mu_{32}\mu_{12}}\times \tag{128}$$

$$\times\frac{1}{\left\{1+\eta_{32}\cos 2k_3(x_2-x)+[\eta_{32}+\cos 2k_3(x_2-x)]\,\eta_{21}\cos 2k_2l_2-\frac{\eta_{21}}{\mu_{32}}\sin 2k_3(x_2-x)\sin 2k_2l_2\right\}}$$

and for the pressure wave:

$$\alpha'_{3T}=k_3\times$$

$$\times\frac{\eta_{32}\sin 2k_3(x_2-x)+\eta_{21}\sin 2k_3(x_2-x)\cos 2k_2l_2+\frac{\eta_{21}}{\mu_{32}}\sin 2k_2l_2\cos 2k_3(x_2-x)}{1-\eta_{32}\cos 2k_3(x_2-x)+[\eta_{32}-\cos 2k_3(x_2-x)]\cdot\eta_{21}\cos 2k_2l_2+\frac{\eta_{21}}{\mu_{32}}\sin 2k_3(x_2-x)\cdot\sin 2k_2l_2};$$

$$\beta'_{3T}=\frac{k_3}{\mu_{32}\mu_{12}}\times \tag{129}$$

$$\times\frac{1}{\left\{1-\eta_{32}\cos 2k_3(x_2-x)+[\eta_{32}-\cos 2k_3(x_2-x)]\,\eta_{21}\cos 2k_2l_2+\frac{\eta_{21}}{\mu_{32}}\sin 2k_3(x_2-x)\sin 2k_2l_2\right\}},$$

where we have, by definition:

$$\mu_{ij}=\frac{W_i^2+W_j^2}{2W_i\cdot W_j};\quad \eta_{ij}=\frac{W_i^2-W_j^2}{W_i^2+W_j^2}.$$

Since we are mainly interested in the distribution of the differential velocities of propagation c', we obtain the formulas for determining c'_{3V} and c'_{3T} by substituting β'_{3V} and β'_{3T} into (76):

$$c'_{3V}=c_3\mu_{32}\mu_{12}\Big[1+\eta_{32}\eta_{21}\cos 2k_2l_2+(\eta_{32}+\eta_{21}\cos 2k_2l_2)\cdot\cos 2k_3(x_2-x)-$$
$$-\frac{\eta_{21}}{\mu_{32}}\sin 2k_3(x_2-x)\sin 2k_2l_2\Big];$$

$$c'_{3T}=c_3\mu_{32}\mu_{12}\Big[1+\eta_{32}\eta_{21}\cos 2k_2l_2-(\eta_{32}+\eta_{21}\cos 2k_2l_2)\cdot\cos 2k_3(x_2-x)+$$
$$+\frac{\eta_{21}}{\mu_{32}}\sin 2k_3(x_2-x)\sin 2k_2l_2\Big]. \tag{130}$$

Consider a few particular cases.

1) Suppose that the second medium presents a wave impedance equal to the geometric mean of the wave impedances of the in-between layers, i.e., $W_2=\sqrt{W_1W_3}$, and, in addition, there is room for a quarter wavelength in the second medium at some frequency ω_1, i.e., $l_2=\frac{\lambda_2}{4}$, then $k_2l_2=\frac{\pi}{2}$. In that case, the differential propagation constants (125) become greatly simplified and equal to:

$$\vec{D}_{3V}(x)=\vec{D}_{3T}(x)=0+i\frac{\omega}{c_3} \tag{131}$$

for all values of x from $-\infty$ to x_2. This points to the absence of reflection of the wave from interfaces x_2 and x_3 in medium *3*. From the theory of electrical transmission lines, we know that this insertion of a medium *2*, under the conditions specified above, matches the wave impedance presented by media *1* and *3* and at the same time sets up the conditions for the complete passage of the wave without attenuation from medium *3* into medium *1*.

Figure 9 shows, for the particular case above, a graph of the distribution of the differential velocities down the waveguide, i.e., c'_V ; c'_T and c'_Q. In medium 2, the integral velocity over the baseline $x_3 - x_2$ is equal to the computed velocity for that medium, i.e. c_2.

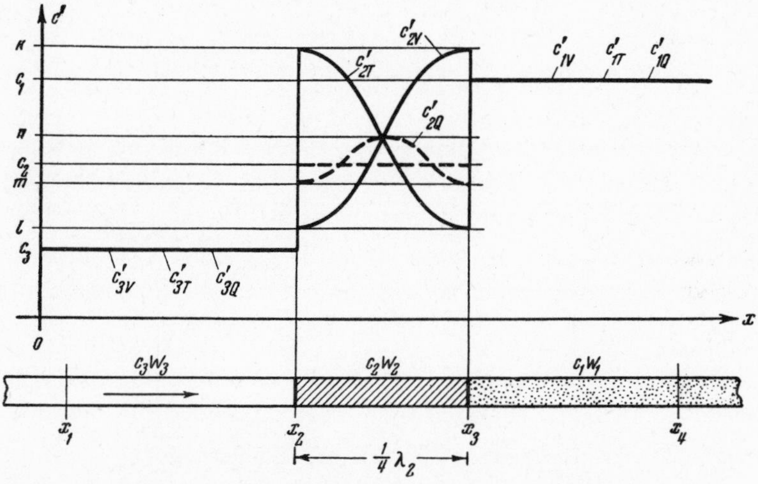

Fig. 9. Distribution of the differential velocities of propagation c' of the velocity wave $\bar{V}$, pressure wave $\bar{T}$, and intensity wave $\bar{Q}$, for the case of a quarter-wavelength "inserted" layer (medium 2) and the impedance relation $W_2 = \sqrt{W_1 W_3}$ $(W_3 > W_1)$. Points k, l, m and n on the ordinate correspond to the following values of c'_3: $k = c_2 \frac{W_2}{W_1}$; $l = c_2 \frac{W_1}{W_2}$; $m = c_2 \frac{2W_1 W_2}{W_1^2 + W_2^2}$; $n = c_2 \frac{W_1^2 + W_2^2}{2W_1 W_2}$.

Then the integral velocity over the baseline $x_1 - x_4$ will be determined on the basis of the formula for the average velocities in geometric seismics, despite the mismatching of the wave impedances. For other frequencies [with the exclusion of those frequencies at which the relations obtaining in the second medium will be $l_2 = \frac{\lambda_2}{4}(2n - 1)$, where $n = 1, 2, 3\ldots$], the formula for the average velocities will break down in its conventional form.

2) We investigated the variation in the differential velocities at the point O in the vicinity of the interface at x_2 (cf. Fig. 8) in response to a change in the frequency ω. For this purpose, we put $(x_2 - x) \to 0$ in formulas (130), which gives us:

$$\left.\begin{aligned} c'_{3V} &= c_3 \frac{W_3}{W_2} \mu_{21} (1 + \eta_{21} \cos 2k_2 l_2) = f_V(\omega, l_2); \\ c'_{3T} &= c_3 \frac{W_2}{W_3} \mu_{21} (1 - \eta_{21} \cos 2k_2 l_2) = f_T(\omega, l_2). \end{aligned}\right\} \quad (132)$$

We then determine the velocity c'_{3Q} for the intensity wave, making use of the equations $\beta'_Q = \frac{1}{2}(\beta'_V + \beta'_T)$; $c' = \frac{\omega}{\beta_1}$ or $c'_Q = \frac{2}{\frac{1}{c'_V} + \frac{1}{c'_T}}$:

$$c'_{3Q} = \frac{c_3 \left[1 + \mu_{21}^2 \left(1 - \eta_{21}^2 \cos 4k_2 l_2\right)\right]}{2\mu_{32}\mu_{21} (1 + \eta_{32}\eta_{21} \cos 2k_2 l_2)}. \quad (133)$$

Figure 10 presents graphs of the variation in the velocity c'_{3V}; c'_{3T} and c'_{3Q} at point O in medium 3 (cf. Fig. 8), based on (132) and (133), with the particular assumption that $W_3 : W_2 : W_1 = 3 : 2 : 1$.

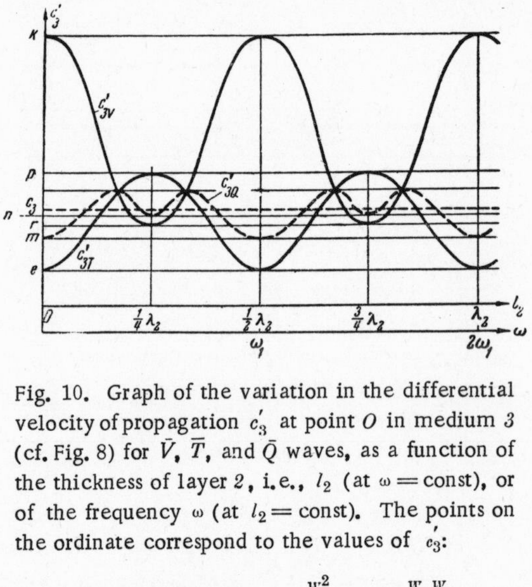

Fig. 10. Graph of the variation in the differential velocity of propagation c'_3 at point O in medium 3 (cf. Fig. 8) for $\bar{V}$, $\bar{T}$, and $\bar{Q}$ waves, as a function of the thickness of layer 2, i.e., l_2 (at $\omega = \text{const}$), or of the frequency ω (at $l_2 = \text{const}$). The points on the ordinate correspond to the values of c'_3:

$$k = c_3 \frac{W_3}{W_1}; \; l = c_3 \frac{W_1}{W_3}; \; p = c_3 \frac{W_2^2}{W_1 W_3}; \; r = c_3 \frac{W_1 W_3}{W_2^2};$$

$$n = c_3 \frac{2W_2^2 W_1 W_3}{W_2^4 + W_1^2 W_3^2}; \; m = c_3 \frac{2W_1 W_3}{W_1^2 + W_3^2}.$$

From the graphs, we see that the differential velocities near the interface x_2 vary strongly as a function of the wave impedance relationships in the media, W_3; W_2; W_1. Other conditions being equal, while, in response to a variation in the frequency ω (or likewise, a variation in l_2), a periodic behavior is experienced, being some multiple of the angular frequency $\omega_1 = \frac{\pi c_2}{l_2}$. In the case where the wave impedance of medium *2* is related by the equation $W_2 = \sqrt{W_1 W_3}$ and a quarter wavelength is accommodated in the second medium, i.e., $l_2 = \frac{\lambda_2}{4}$ or $\frac{\omega_1}{2}$, the differential velocities of all of the modes will be equal.

3) We investigated the distribution of the differential velocities in a nonhomogeneous medium (Fig. 8) as a function of the distance x. For that purpose, we present formulas (130) in modified form:

$$\left.\begin{aligned} c'_{3V} &= c_3\mu_{32}\mu_{21}\,[A + B\cdot\cos 2k_3(x_2 - x) - C\cdot\sin 2k_3(x_2 - x)];\\ c'_{3T} &= c_3\mu_{32}\mu_{21}\,[A - B\cdot\cos 2k_3(x_2 - x) + C\cdot\sin 2k_3(x_2 - x)], \end{aligned}\right\} \quad (134)$$

where we have, by definition:

$$A = 1 + \eta_{32}\eta_{21}\cos 2k_2 l_2;\quad B = \eta_{32} + \eta_{21}\cos\, 2k_2 l_2;\quad C = \frac{\eta_{21}}{\mu_{32}}\sin 2k_2 l_2.$$

Consider two cases where, between the length l_2 and the wavelength in that medium, i.e., λ_2, the following relations hold:

a) $l_2 = \frac{\lambda_2}{2}n$, where $n = 0, 1, 2, 3 \ldots$ The values of the symbols A, B and C become equal $(2k_2 l_2 = 2\pi n)$ to the following:

$$A = 1 + \eta_{32}\eta_{21};\; B = \eta_{32} + \eta_{21};\; C = 0, \quad (135)$$

while the differential velocities in medium *3* take on the values:

$$\left.\begin{aligned} c'_{3V} &= c_3\mu_{31}\,[1 + \eta_{31}\cos 2k_3(x_2 - x)] = f_V(\omega, x);\\ c'_{3T} &= c_3\mu_{31}\,[1 - \eta_{31}\cos 2k_3(x_2 - x)] = f_T(\omega, x). \end{aligned}\right\} \quad (136)$$

In comparing the equations so obtained with (78), we arrive at the conclusion that, in the case under study, the distribution of the differential velocities in the third medium will be the same as in Fig. 5. If $n = 0$, then the thickness of the layer $l_2 = 0$ and the medium (Fig. 8) will be similar to that considered in the preceding section. In all remaining cases, $n = 1, 2, 3 \ldots$, where a multiple of the half wavelengths are accommodated in the second medium, the effect of the second medium on the third is not felt and is above all not exerted on the distribution of the differential velocities and on α'_{3V} ; α'_{3T} for any impedance relationships W_1; W_2; W_3. In other words, the reflected wave in medium *3* is exclusively determined by the relationship between wave impedances W_1 and W_3, and is independent of W_2 for the relations between l_2 and λ_2 as referred to above, i.e., it may be assumed that the second medium is absent.

Figure 11a shows a graph of the distribution of c'_{3V} and c'_{3T}, as well as of c'_{2V} and c'_{2T} for an inhomogeneous waveguide (Fig. 8), assuming $l_2 = \frac{\lambda_2}{2}$ and $W_3 : W_2 : W_1 = 3 : 2 : 1$, where $c_1 = c_2 = c_3$.

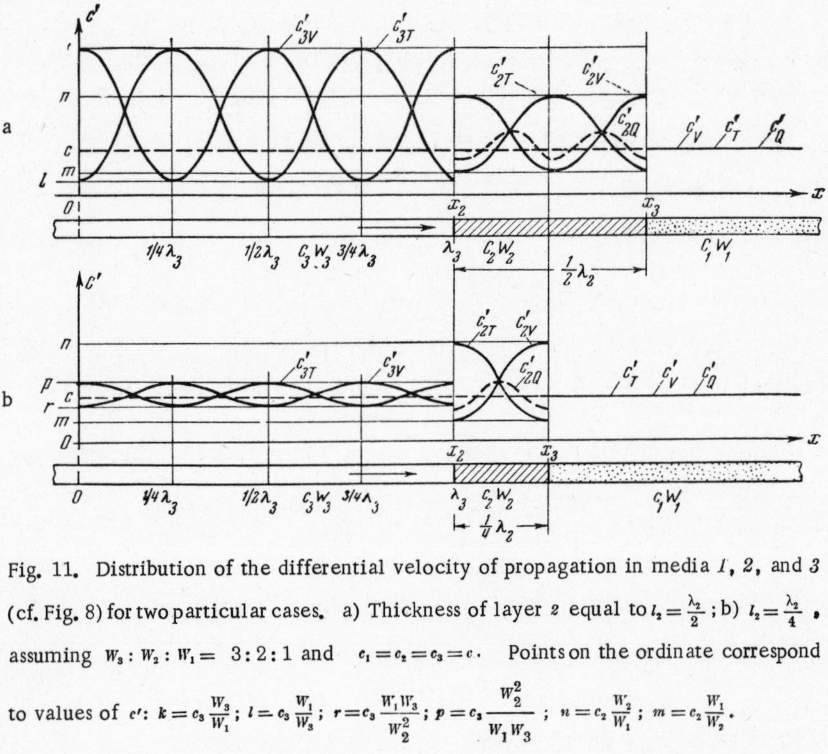

Fig. 11. Distribution of the differential velocity of propagation in media *1*, *2*, and *3* (cf. Fig. 8) for two particular cases. a) Thickness of layer *2* equal to $l_2 = \frac{\lambda_2}{2}$; b) $l_2 = \frac{\lambda_2}{4}$, assuming $W_3 : W_2 : W_1 = 3:2:1$ and $c_1 = c_2 = c_3 = c$. Points on the ordinate correspond to values of c': $k = c_3 \frac{W_3}{W_1}$; $l = c_3 \frac{W_1}{W_3}$; $r = c_3 \frac{W_1 W_3}{W_2^2}$; $p = c_3 \frac{W_2^2}{W_1 W_3}$; $n = c_2 \frac{W_2}{W_1}$; $m = c_2 \frac{W_1}{W_2}$.

b) $l_2 = \frac{\lambda_2}{4}(2n - 1)$, where $n = 1, 2, 3, \ldots$ In that case, the definitions given in (134) become equal $[2k_2 l_2 = \pi(2n - 1)]$ to:

$$A = 1 - \eta_{32}\eta_{21};\quad B = \eta_{32} - \eta_{21};\quad C = 0. \tag{137}$$

Substitution of those values into (134) yields:

$$\left.\begin{aligned} c'_{3V} &= c_3 \mu_{32} \mu_{21} [1 - \eta_{32}\eta_{21} + (\eta_{32} - \eta_{21}) \cos 2k_3 (x_2 - x)]; \\ c'_{3T} &= c_3 \mu_{32} \mu_{21} [1 - \eta_{32}\eta_{21} + (\eta_{32} - \eta_{21}) \cos 2k_3 (x_2 - x)]; \end{aligned}\right\} \tag{138}$$

or, eventually, after a series of transformations, the differential velocities in the third medium:

$$\left.\begin{aligned} c'_{3V} &= c_3\left[\frac{W_1W_3}{2W_2^2}+\frac{W_2^2}{2W_1W_3}+\left(\frac{W_1W_3}{2W_2^2}-\frac{W_2^2}{2W_1W_3}\right)\cos 2k_3(x_2-x)\right], \\ c'_{3T} &= c_3\left[\frac{W_1W_3}{2W_2^2}+\frac{W_2^2}{2W_1W_3}-\left(\frac{W_1W_3}{2W_2^2}-\frac{W_2^2}{2W_1W_3}\right)\cos 2k_3(x_2-x)\right]. \end{aligned}\right\} \quad (139)$$

According to the formulas so obtained (139), a graph is plotted in Fig. 11b for the distribution of the differential velocities in the waveguide (Fig. 8) for the particular case under consideration, $l_2=\frac{\lambda_2}{4}$, assuming $W_3:W_2:W_1=$ 3 : 2 : 1. We see from the graph that the differential velocity of a pressure wave, in the third medium near the interface, is greater than that of a velocity wave, although, for an interface of that type, when $W_3>W_2$, we have the reverse relationship between the velocities in the case of a waveguide with a single interface (cf. section 3 and Fig. 5). The effect of the succeeding interface, i.e., x_3 (see Fig. 8), is manifested precisely in that fact.

4) Consider, finally, the case where $W_1=W_3$. Under that condition, coefficients μ and η assume values:

$$\mu_{32}=\mu_{21};\quad \eta_{32}=-\eta_{21}, \quad (140)$$

while (130) are rearranged in the following form (putting $c_1=c_3$)

$$c'_{3V}=c_1\mu_{12}^2\,[1-\eta_{12}^2\cos 2k_2l_2+(1-\cos 2k_2l_2)\,\eta_{12}\cos 2k_1(x_2-x)+ \\ +\frac{\eta_{12}}{\mu_{12}}\sin 2k_2l_2\sin 2k_1(x_2-x)\Big];$$

$$c'_{3T}=c_1\mu_{12}^2\,[1-\eta_{12}^2\cos 2k_2l_2-(1-\cos 2k_2l_2)\,\eta_{12}\cos 2k_1(x_2-x)- \\ -\frac{\eta_{12}}{\mu_{12}}\sin 2k_2l_2\sin 2k_1(x_2-x)\Big]. \quad (141a)$$

We next investigate the variation in the differential velocities in the vicinity of the interface x at a point O, as a function of the variation in the frequency ω or in the thickness l_2 of the second layer. In that case, equations (141) are rewritten in the following form, putting $(x_2-x)\to 0$:

$$c'_{3V} = c_1 \frac{W_1^2 + W_2^2}{2W_2^2}\left(1 - \frac{W_1^2 - W_2^2}{W_1^2 + W_2^2}\cos 2k_2 l_2\right) = f_V(\omega,\ l_2);$$

$$c'_{3T} = c_1 \frac{W_1^2 + W_2^2}{2W_2^2}\left(1 + \frac{W_1^2 - W_2^2}{W_1^2 + W_2^2}\cos 2k_2 l_2\right) = f_T(\omega, l_2). \qquad (141b)$$

In conformity with these formulas, assuming l_2 or ω to be variable quantities, we have plotted in Fig. 12 graphs of the variation in the differential velocities at point O of the third medium for pressure and velocity waves. It is characteristic that c'_{3V} at point O, when $W_1 > W_2$, is greater than or equal to the computed velocity in that medium, i.e., c_1, while, for the pressure wave c'_{3T} is always less than or equal to the computed velocity c_1. For the reverse wave impedance relationship, i.e., $W_2 > W_1$, we will have the reverse relationship between velocities c'_{3V} and c'_{3T}.

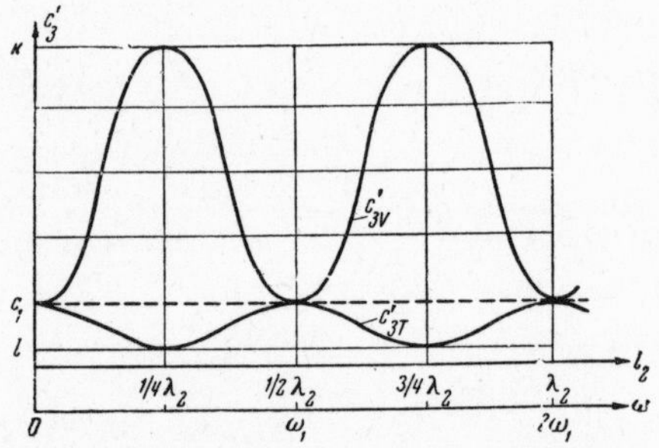

Fig. 12. Graphs of the variation in the differential velocity of propagation c'_3 at point O near the interface x_2 (see Fig. 8) for $\bar{V}$ and $\bar{T}$ waves, as a function of variation in the thickness of the second layer, l_2, when ω = = const, or as a function of frequency ω, when l_2 = const (cf. Fig. 10). It is assumed that $W_1 > W_2$ ($W_1 = W_3$; $c_1 = c_3$). The points on the ordinate correspond to values of c':

$$k = c_1 \frac{W_1^2}{W_2^2};\ l = c_1 \frac{W_2^2}{W_1^2}.$$

For the case under consideration $W_1 = W_3$ and $c_1 = c_3$, we investigate the distribution of differential velocities with the distance x for two particular cases:

a) $l_2 = \frac{\lambda_2}{2} n$, where $n = 0, 1, 2, 3, \ldots$ and the formulas for the differential velocities in the third medium (cf. Fig. 8) (140) take on the form $(2k_2 l_2 = 2\pi n)$:

$$\left.\begin{aligned} c'_{3V} &= c\,\mu_{12}^2\left(1 - \eta_{12}^2\right) = c_1 = f_V(x,\ \omega); \\ c'_{3T} &= c_1 \mu_{12}^2\left(1 - \eta_{12}^2\right) = c_1 = f_T(x,\ \omega). \end{aligned}\right\} \qquad (142)$$

Consequently, the differential velocities for all values of x in the third medium remain constant and equal to c_1, and by computing α'_{3V} and α'_{3T}, we find that they vanish. This bears witness to the fact that the wave fully penetrates through the second medium without suffering reflection. The distribution of the differential velocities in the waveguide under study is given in Fig. 13; it is there assumed that:

$$l_2 = \frac{\lambda_2}{2}; \quad W_1 : W_2 = 2:1.$$

b) $l_2 = \frac{\lambda_2}{4}(2n-1)$, where $n = 1, 2, 3, \ldots$ In that case, equations (140) take on the values $[2k_2 l_2 = \pi(2n-1)]$:

$$\left.\begin{aligned} c'_{3V} &= c_1 \mu_{12}^2 \left[1 + \eta_{12}^2 + 2\eta_{12}^2 \cos 2k_1 (x_2 - x)\right] = f_V(x, \omega); \\ c'_{3T} &= c_1 \mu_{12}^2 \left[1 + \eta_{12}^2 - 2\eta_{12}^2 \cos 2k_1 (x_2 - x)\right] = f_T(x, \omega). \end{aligned}\right\} \tag{143}$$

According to the formulas so obtained, we have plotted in Fig. 14 graphs giving the distribution of the differential velocities for velocity, pressure, and intensity waves, assuming $W_1 : W_2 = 2:1$.

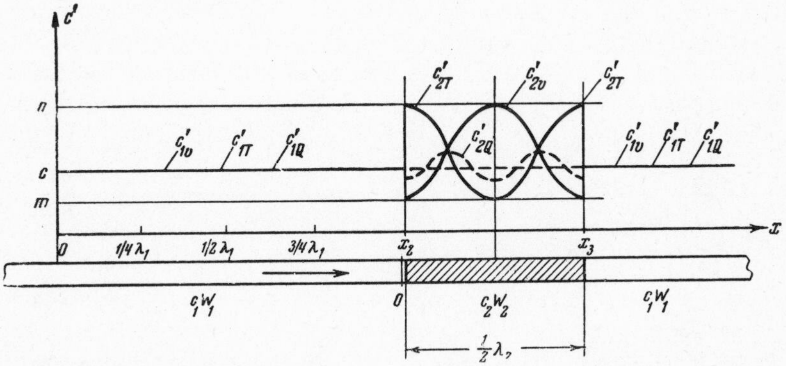

Fig. 13. Distribution of the differential velocities of propagation c' in media *1*, *2*, and *1* for the particular case where the thickness of layer *2* is $l_2 = \frac{\lambda_2}{2}$. It is assumed that $W_1 > W_2$ and $c_1 = c_2 = c\ (W_1 = W_3;\ c_1 = c_3)$. Points on the ordinate correspond to values of c': $m = c\frac{W_2}{W_1}$; $n = c\frac{W_1}{W_2}$.

Integral Wave Characteristics

The integral propagation constants over a given baseline, say $x_1 - x_4$ (cf. Fig. 8), are determined by the same method of integrating $\vec{D}_V$:

$$\vec{S}_V = \int_{x_1}^{x_2} \vec{D}_{3V} dx + \int_{x_2}^{x_3} \vec{D}_{2V} dx + \int_{x_3}^{x_4} \vec{D}_{1V} dx. \tag{144}$$

For pressure waves, we integrate the differential propagation constants $\vec{D}_T$:

$$\vec{S}_T = \int_{x_1}^{x_2} \vec{D}_{3T} dx + \int_{x_2}^{x_3} \vec{D}_{2T} dx + \int_{x_3}^{x_4} \vec{D}_{1T} dx, \qquad (145)$$

where $\vec{D}_{3V}$; $\vec{D}_{2V}$; $\vec{D}_{1V}$ are the differential propagation constants for a velocity wave for media *3*, *2* and *1*, respectively; $\vec{D}_{3T}$; $\vec{D}_{2T}$; $\vec{D}_{1T}$ are the differential propagation constants of a pressure wave for media *3*, *2*, and *1*, respectively.

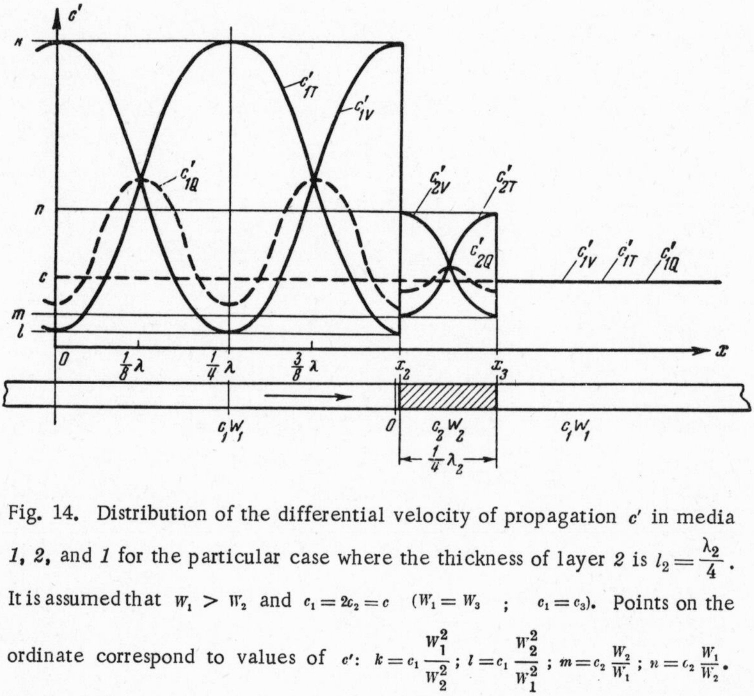

Fig. 14. Distribution of the differential velocity of propagation c' in media *1*, *2*, and *1* for the particular case where the thickness of layer *2* is $l_2 = \frac{\lambda_2}{4}$. It is assumed that $W_1 > W_2$ and $c_1 = 2c_2 = c$ $(W_1 = W_3$; $c_1 = c_3)$. Points on the ordinate correspond to values of c': $k = c_1 \frac{W_1^2}{W_2^2}$; $l = c_1 \frac{W_2^2}{W_1^2}$; $m = c_2 \frac{W_2}{W_1}$; $n = c_2 \frac{W_1}{W_2}$.

We find the value of the integral propagation constant of a velocity wave, $\vec{S}_V$. For this purpose, we may present $\vec{D}_V$ in terms of the input impedance of the waveguide $\vec{Z}$, in conformity with (16):

$$\vec{S}_V = \bar{q}_{03} \int_{x_1}^{x_2} \frac{\vec{Z}_3(x)}{\overline{W}_3} dx + \bar{q}_{02} \int_{x_2}^{x_3} \frac{\vec{Z}_2(x)}{\overline{W}_2} dx + \bar{q}_{01} \int_{x_3}^{x_4} \frac{\overline{W}_1}{\overline{W}_1} dx. \qquad (146)$$

Substituting the values of the input impedances (121, 122), we obtain:

$$\vec{S}_V = \bar{q}_{03}\int_{x_1}^{x_2} \frac{H_{23} + \operatorname{th}\bar{q}_{03}(x_2 - x)}{H_{23}\cdot\operatorname{th}\bar{q}_{03}(x_2 - x) + 1}\,dx +$$

$$+ \bar{q}_{02}\int_{x_2}^{x_3} \frac{n_{12} + \operatorname{th}\bar{q}_{02}(x_3 - x)}{n_{12}\cdot\operatorname{th}\bar{q}_{02}(x_3 - x) + 1}\,dx + \bar{q}_{01}(x_4 - x_3), \quad (147)$$

where, by definition: $H_{23} = \frac{\vec{Z}_2(l_2)}{\overline{W}_3} = n_{23}\frac{n_{12} + \operatorname{th}\bar{q}_{02}l_2}{n_{12}\cdot\operatorname{th}\bar{q}_{02}l_2 + 1}$; $n_{12} = \frac{\overline{W}_1}{\overline{W}_2}$; $n_{23} = \frac{\overline{W}_2}{\overline{W}_3}$.

The general form of the integrals (147) coincides with the form of the integral in (85), whose solution is found as we write the result:

$$\vec{S}_V = \ln\left[\frac{1 - H_{23}}{2}e^{-\bar{q}_{03}(x_2 - x_1)} + \frac{1 + H_{23}}{2}e^{\bar{q}_{03}(x_2 - x_1)}\right] +$$

$$+ \ln\left[\frac{1 - n_{12}}{2}e^{-\bar{q}_{02}(x_3 - x_2)} + \frac{1 + n_{12}}{2}e^{\bar{q}_{02}(x_3 - x_2)}\right] + \bar{q}_{01}(x_4 - x_3). \quad (148)$$

Substituting the values $x_2 - x_1 = l_3$; $x_3 - x_2 = l_2$; $x_4 - x_3 = l$, we get:

$$\vec{S}_V = \ln\left[\left(\frac{1 - H_{23}}{2}e^{-\bar{q}_{03}l_3} + \frac{1 + H_{23}}{2}e^{\bar{q}_{03}l_3}\right)\left(\frac{1 - n_{12}}{2}e^{-\bar{q}_{02}l_2} + \right.\right.$$

$$\left.\left. + \frac{1 + n_{12}}{2}e^{\bar{q}_{02}l_2}\right)e^{+\bar{q}_{01}l_1}\right]. \quad (149)$$

Making use of the familiar relationships of hyperbolic functions:

$$e^x = \operatorname{ch} x + \operatorname{sh} x; \qquad e^{-x} = \operatorname{ch} x - \operatorname{sh} x, \quad (150)$$

we express the integral propagation constant in terms of hyperbolic functions:

$$\vec{S}_V = \ln[(\operatorname{ch}\bar{q}_{03}l_3 + H_{23}\operatorname{sh}\bar{q}_{03}l_3)(\operatorname{ch}\bar{q}_{02}l_2 + n_{12}\operatorname{sh}\bar{q}_{02}l_2)(\operatorname{ch}\bar{q}_{01}l_1 + \operatorname{sh}\bar{q}_{01}l_1)], \quad (151)$$

or, substituting the value of H_{23}, we obtain, after cumbersome algebraic transformations:

$$\vec{S}_V = \ln\{[(\operatorname{ch}\bar{q}_{02}l_2 + n_{12}\operatorname{sh}\bar{q}_{02}l_2)\operatorname{ch}\bar{q}_{03}l_3 + n_{23}(n_{12}\operatorname{ch}q_{02}l_2 +$$

$$+ \operatorname{sh}\bar{q}_{02}l_2)\operatorname{sh}\bar{q}_{03}l_3](\operatorname{ch}\bar{q}_{01}l_1 + \operatorname{sh}\bar{q}_{01}l_1)\}. \quad (152)$$

In a similar manner, we find the integral propagation constant over the baseline $\Delta x_{14} = x_4 - x_1$ (Fig. 8) for the pressure wave $\vec{S}_T$. For that purpose, we express $\vec{D}_T$ in (145) in terms of the values of the input impedances $\vec{Z}$:

$$\vec{S}_T = \bar{q}_{03}\int_{x_1}^{2} \frac{\overline{W}_3}{\vec{Z}_3(x)}\,dx + \bar{q}_{02}\int_{x_2}^{x_3} \frac{\overline{W}_2}{\vec{Z}_2(x)}\,dx + \bar{q}_{01}\int_{x_3}^{x_4} \frac{\overline{W}_1}{\vec{Z}_1(x)}\,dx, \quad (153)$$

or, by availing ourselves of (121, 122), we find:

$$\vec{S}_T=\bar{q}_{03}\int_{x_1}^{x_2}\frac{H_{32}+\text{th}\,\bar{q}_{03}(x_2-x)}{H_{32}\cdot\text{th}\,\bar{q}_{03}(x_2-x)+1}\,dx+$$

$$+\bar{q}_{02}\int_{x_2}^{x_3}\frac{n_{21}+\text{th}\,\bar{q}_{02}(x_3-x)}{n_{21}\cdot\text{th}\,\bar{q}_{02}(x_3-x)+1}\,dx+\bar{q}_{01}(x_4-x_3), \quad (154)$$

where, by definition:

$$H_{32}=\frac{1}{H_{23}}=n_{32}\frac{n_{21}+\text{th}\,\bar{q}_{02}l_2}{n_{21}\cdot\text{th}\,\bar{q}_{02}l_2+1};\quad n_{21}=\frac{1}{n_{12}}=\frac{\overline{W}_2}{\overline{W}_1};\quad n_{32}=\frac{\overline{W}_3}{\overline{W}_2}.$$

Since we have, again, typical integrals [cf. (85)], we write the result as:

$$\vec{S}_T=\ln\left[\frac{1-H_{32}}{2}e^{-\bar{q}_{03}l_3}+\frac{1+H_{32}}{2}e^{\bar{q}_{03}l_3}\right]+$$

$$+\ln\left[\frac{1-n_{21}}{2}e^{-\bar{q}_{02}l_2}+\frac{1+n_{21}}{2}e^{\bar{q}_{02}l_2}\right]+\bar{q}_{01}l_1. \quad (155)$$

Similarly to the preceding case, expressing $\vec{S}_T$ in terms of hyperbolic functions, we obtain, after a series of transformations:

$$\vec{S}_T=\ln\{[(\text{ch}\,\bar{q}_{02}l_2+n_{21}\,\text{sh}\,\bar{q}_{02}l_2)\,\text{ch}\,\bar{q}_{03}l_3+$$

$$+n_{32}(n_{21}\,\text{ch}\,\bar{q}_{02}l_2+\text{sh}\,q_{02}l_2)\,\text{sh}\,\bar{q}_{03}l_3]\,(\text{ch}\bar{q}_{01}l_1+\text{sh}\,\bar{q}_{01}l_1)\}. \quad (156)$$

The integral propagation constants[1] for velocity waves (152) and pressure waves (156) enable us to study the transmission of the waves through layer *2*, when different media[2] are layered on to the right and to the left of layer *2*.

For the steady-state mode of oscillations $(p=i\omega)$, the integral propagation constants over the baseline Δx_{14} (152, 156) take on the following form:

$$\left.\begin{aligned}\vec{S}_V&=\ln[(\cos k_2l_2\cdot\cos k_3l_3-n_{23}\sin k_2l_2\cdot\sin k_3l_3)+\\&\quad+i(n_{12}\cdot\sin k_2l_2\cos k_3l_3+n_{13}\cos k_2l_2\sin k_3l_3)]+ik_1l_1;\\\vec{S}_T&=\ln[(\cos k_2l_2\cdot\cos k_3l_3-n_{32}\sin k_2l_2\cdot\sin k_3l_3)+\\&\quad+i(n_{21}\sin k_2l_2\cdot\cos k_3l_3+n_{31}\cos k_2l_2\sin k_3l_3)]+ik_1l_1.\end{aligned}\right\}\quad(157)$$

[1] The integral propagation constants over the baseline $x_1 - x_4$(see Fig. 8) may be obtained by another approach, using the conventional two-terminal-pair network technique. This approach, even in the particular case $W_1=W_3$, involves cumbersome and tedious transformations. However, the approach has been carried through, yielding the same results.

[2] A more general case for the transmission of waves through a hard layer at different angles of incidence is treated by B. D. Tartakovskii [24] (involving sinusoidal waves, with resistive losses absent).

Separating real and imaginary parts, we obtain the values of the integral phase constants and attenuation constants over the baseline Δx_{14}:

$$\left.\begin{aligned}
&\beta_V = \operatorname{arctg}\left(\frac{n_{12}\operatorname{tg}k_2l_2 + n_{13}\operatorname{tg}k_3l_3}{1 - n_{23}\operatorname{tg}k_2l_2\cdot\operatorname{tg}k_3l_3}\right) + k_1l_1;\\
&\beta_T = \operatorname{arctg}\left(\frac{n_{21}\operatorname{tg}k_2l_2 + n_{31}\operatorname{tg}k_3l_3}{1 - n_{32}\operatorname{tg}k_2l_2\cdot\operatorname{tg}k_3l_3}\right) + k_1l_1;\\
&\ln\left(\frac{V_{x_1}}{V_{x_4}}\right) = \alpha_V =\\
&\ln\sqrt{(\cos k_2l_2\cdot\cos k_3l_3 - n_{23}\cdot\sin k_2l_2\sin k_3l_3)^2 + (n_{12}\cdot\sin k_2l_2\cdot\cos k_3l_3 + n_{13}\cos k_2l_2\sin k_3l_3)^2};\\
&\ln\left(\frac{T_{x_1}}{T_{x_4}}\right) = \alpha_T =\\
&\ln\sqrt{(\cos k_2l_2\cdot\cos k_3l_3 - n_{32}\cdot\sin k_2l_2\cdot\sin k_3l_3)^2 + (n_{21}\cdot\sin k_2l_2\cdot\cos k_3l_3 + n_{31}\cdot\cos k_2l_2\cdot\sin k_3l_3)^2},
\end{aligned}\right\} \quad (158)$$

where, by definition: $k_1 = \frac{\omega}{c_1} = \frac{2\pi}{\lambda_1}$; $k_2 = \frac{\omega}{c_2} = \frac{2\pi}{\lambda_2}$; $k_3 = \frac{\omega}{c_3} = \frac{2\pi}{\lambda_3}$ (wave numbers); $n_{ij} = \frac{W_i}{W_j}$.

We now determine, finally, the integral velocities over the baseline Δx_{14}, making use of (95):

$$\left.\begin{aligned}
c_{SV} &= \frac{\Delta x_{14}\cdot\omega}{\beta_V} = \frac{l_1 + l_2 + l_3}{\frac{1}{\omega}\cdot\left[\pi n + \operatorname{arctg}\left(\frac{n_{12}\operatorname{tg}k_2l_2 + n_{13}\operatorname{tg}k_3l_3}{1 - n_{23}\operatorname{tg}k_2l_2\cdot\operatorname{tg}k_3l_3}\right)\right] + \frac{l_1}{c_1}},\\
c_{ST} &= \frac{\Delta x_{14}\cdot\omega}{\beta_T} = \frac{l_1 + l_2 + l_3}{\frac{1}{\omega}\cdot\left[\pi n + \operatorname{arctg}\left(\frac{n_{21}\cdot\operatorname{tg}k_2l_2 + n_{31}\operatorname{tg}k_3l_3}{1 - n_{32}\operatorname{tg}k_2l_2\cdot\operatorname{tg}k_3l_3}\right)\right] + \frac{l_1}{c_1}},
\end{aligned}\right\} \quad (159)$$

where $n = 1, 2, 3, \ldots$ as a function of the number of half wavelengths accommodated in media *2* and *3*.

Consider several particular values of $\vec{S}_V$ and $\vec{S}_T$.

1) Suppose that the wave impedances are related by the following equation: $W_2 = \sqrt{W_1W_3}$; while, in the second medium, at some frequency ω, a quarter wavelength is accommodated, i.e., $l = \frac{\lambda_2}{4}$. In that case, (157) are greatly simplified:

$$\left.\begin{aligned}
\vec{S}_V &= \ln\left(\frac{\overline{V}_{x_1}}{\overline{V}_{x_4}}\right) = \ln\left(\frac{W_1}{W_2}\right) + i\beta_0;\\
\vec{S}_T &= \ln\left(\frac{\overline{T}_{x_1}}{\overline{T}_{x_4}}\right) = \ln\left(\frac{W_2}{W_1}\right) + i\beta_0;
\end{aligned}\right\} \quad (160)$$

where $\beta_0 = k_3l_3 + k_2l_2 + k_1l_1$ and signifies the phase shift experienced over the baseline Δx_{14}, which will take place in the case where the wave impedances are equal, $W_1 = W_2 = W_3$. For the intensity wave, over the baseline Δx_{14}, we find:

$$\vec{S}_Q = \frac{1}{2}(\vec{S}_V + \vec{S}_T) = \frac{1}{2}\ln\left(\frac{\overline{V}_{x_1}\cdot\overline{T}_{x_1}}{\overline{V}_{x_4}\cdot\overline{T}_{x_4}}\right) = 0 + i\beta_0. \qquad (161)$$

and, accordingly, the intensity wave passes down layer *2* without suffering attenuation of the energy it carries (without reflections), while the velocity wave and the pressure wave are transformed while traversing the second medium, as follows:

$$\frac{\overline{V}_{x_1}}{\overline{V}_{x_4}} = \frac{W_1}{W_2} = \sqrt{\frac{W_1}{W_3}}; \quad \frac{\overline{T}_{x_1}}{\overline{T}_{x_4}} = \frac{W_2}{W_1} = \sqrt{\frac{W_3}{W_1}}. \qquad (162)$$

The integral velocity in that case is:

$$c_S = \frac{\omega(x_4 - x_1)}{\beta_0} = \frac{x_4 - x_1}{\frac{l_3}{c_3} + \frac{l_2}{c_2} + \frac{l_1}{c_1}}, \qquad (163)$$

i.e., it is determined in accord with the generally familiar formula for the mean velocities.

2) Suppose $W_1 = W_3$; $c_1 = c_3$; $l_1 = l_3$. In that case, the integral velocities and the amplitude ratio over the baseline Δx_{14} (see Fig. 8) will be:

$$\left.\begin{aligned}
c_{SV} &= \frac{2l_1 + l_2}{\frac{1}{\omega}\left[\pi n + \operatorname{arctg}\left(\frac{n_{12}\operatorname{tg}k_2l_2 + \operatorname{tg}k_1l_1}{1 - n_{21}\operatorname{tg}k_2l_2\cdot\operatorname{tg}k_1l_1}\right)\right] + \frac{l_1}{c_1}};\\
c_{ST} &= \frac{2l_1 + l_2}{\frac{1}{\omega}\left[\pi n + \operatorname{arctg}\left(\frac{n_{21}\operatorname{tg}k_2l_2 + \operatorname{tg}k_1l_1}{1 - n_{12}\operatorname{tg}k_2l_2\operatorname{tg}k_1l_1}\right)\right] + \frac{l_1}{c_1}};\\
\frac{V_{x_1}}{V_{x_4}} &= \sqrt{(\cos k_2l_2\cdot\cos k_1l_1 - n_{21}\sin k_2l_2\cdot\sin k_1l_1)^2 + (\cos k_2l_2\sin k_1l_1 + n_{12}\cos k_1l_1\sin k_2l_2)^2};\\
\frac{T_{x_1}}{T_{x_4}} &= \sqrt{(\cos k_2l_2\cdot\cos k_1l_1 - n_{12}\sin k_2l_2\cdot\sin k_1l_1)^2 + (\cos k_2l_2\sin k_1l_1 + n_{21}\cos k_1l_1\sin k_2l_2)^2}.
\end{aligned}\right\} \qquad (164)$$

A graph is plotted in Fig. 15, based on (164), indicating the integral velocity and the amplitude ratios of V and T waves, characterizing the macrostructure of the waves in a three-layered medium (Fig. 8). Comparing the graphs of the phase velocities c_S in the case of a single interface (see Fig. 7) and in the case of two interfaces (Fig. 15), we may note their external similarity. However, the graphs of the amplitude ratios of V and T waves in the case of a three-layered medium have a more complex form, although the periodicity in the variation of the amplitude ratios remains the same in that case as in a doubly layered medium.

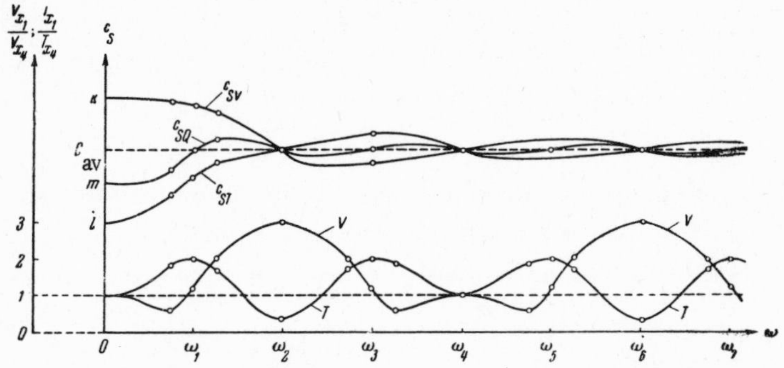

Fig. 15. Macrostructure of the waves. Dispersion of the phase velocities and attenuation of the amplitudes of $\bar{V}$, $\bar{T}$, and $\bar{Q}$ waves over the baseline $x_4 - x_1$ (see Fig. 8) in the case of a three-layered medium. It is assumed that: $W_1 = W_3$; $l_1 = l_3$; $c_1 = c_3$; $W_2 = 3W_1$. Points on the ordinate (k, l, m) correspond to the following values of the integral velocity c_S: $k = c_{av} \frac{3}{2 + n_{12}}$; $l = c_{av} \frac{3}{2 + n_{21}}$; $m = c_{av} \frac{3}{2 + \mu_{12}}$.

Consider two particular cases of integral constants α and β under the assumption $W_1 = W_3$; $l_1 = l_3$; $c_1 = c_3$.

a) In the second medium, there is room for a half wavelength λ_2 or generally $l_2 = \frac{\lambda_2}{2} n$, where $n = 0, 1, 2, 3, \ldots$ Then the integral constants (158) take on values $(k_2 l_2 = \pi \cdot n)$:

$$\left.\begin{aligned} \alpha_V &= 0; \quad \beta_V = 2k_1 l_1 + \pi \cdot n = 2k_1 l_1 + k_2 l_2; \\ \alpha_T &= 0; \quad \beta_T = 2k_1 l_1 + \pi \cdot n = 2k_1 l_1 + k_2 l_2 \end{aligned}\right\} \tag{165}$$

and, consequently, the velocity and pressure waves traverse the second medium without suffering reflections (cf. Fig. 13), while the velocity may be determined on the basis of the formula for average velocities:

$$c_{(x_1 - x_4)} = \frac{\omega (x_4 - x_1)}{2k_1 l_1 + k_2 l_2} = \frac{x_4 - x_1}{\frac{2l_1}{c_1} + \frac{l_2}{c_2}}. \tag{166}$$

b) In the second medium, there is room for a quarter wavelength λ_2 or generally $l_2 = \frac{\lambda_2}{4} (2n - 1)$, where $n = 1, 2, 3, \ldots$ In that case, the integral constants (158) take on the following values $\left(k_2 l_2 = \frac{\pi}{2}\right)$ (cf. Fig. 14):

$$\left.\begin{aligned} \alpha_V &= \ln \sqrt{n_{21}^2 \sin^2 k_1 l_1 + n_{12}^2 \cos^2 k_1 l_1}; \\ \beta_V &= \operatorname{arctg}(-n_{21}^2 \operatorname{ctg} k_1 l_1) + k_1 l_1; \\ \alpha_T &= \ln \sqrt{n_{12}^2 \sin^2 k_1 l_1 + n_{21}^2 \cos^2 k_1 l_1}; \\ \beta_T &= \operatorname{arctg}(-n_{12}^2 \operatorname{ctg} k_1 l_1) + k_1 l_1, \end{aligned}\right\} \tag{167}$$

while, if those constants are determined over the baseline $x_2 - x_3$, i.e., only for the second medium $(k_1 l_1 = 0)$, we get:

$$\left.\begin{aligned} \alpha_V &= \ln(n_{12}); \quad \beta_V = \operatorname{arctg} \infty = \frac{\pi}{2}; \\ \alpha_T &= \ln(n_{21}); \quad \beta_T = \operatorname{arctg} \infty = \frac{\pi}{2}, \end{aligned}\right\} \tag{168}$$

and, consequently, the velocity and pressure waves traverse the second medium at a velocity inherent to that medium, c_2, while the amplitudes of the waves traversing the second medium become transformed, in the case in question, in conformity with the ratios:

$$\frac{\overline{V}_{x_2}}{\overline{V}_{x_3}} = \frac{W_1}{W_2}; \quad \frac{\overline{T}_{x_2}}{\overline{T}_{x_3}} = \frac{W_2}{W_1}. \tag{169}$$

SECTION FIVE

INCIDENCE OF A PLANE WAVE NORMAL TO THE LAYERS OF A PERIODICALLY LAYERED ELASTIC MEDIUM

The cases considered above of the traversal of nonhomogeneous media by sinusoidal waves point out the dependence of the phase velocity of elastic waves on frequency. This frequency dependence becomes especially manifest in the case of periodically and aperiodically layered media. A knowledge of the velocity of propagation and of the conditions governing passage of the wave through similar media is of particular interest, since such layered media are encountered rather frequently in seismic prospecting practice. The solution of the problem relating to periodically layered media for the case of two media in one period of the structure was first given by Kasterin [25] for sinusoidal waves, assuming the elastic layers of the medium to be ideally elastic. The problem under consideration here has been solved, with similar constraints observed, in [26].

In the development of the research alluded to above, this section contains the solution of that same problem (two layers within one period of the structure) for the case of nonsteady-state oscillations, with resistive (absorptive) losses in the layers of the medium taken into account. The general solution of the problem is rendered in operator notation, which makes it possible to use the methods of operational calculus to investigate, e.g., the propagation of a wave impulse in a periodically layered medium. However, only the micro- and macrostructure of the waves, for a sinusoidal mode of oscillations assuming the layers of the medium to be ideally elastic, have been investigated in detailed fashion in the development of this problem as presented here.

At the conclusion of the section, the solution of the problem for the case of an arbitrary number of layers accommodated within one period of the structure is treated briefly.

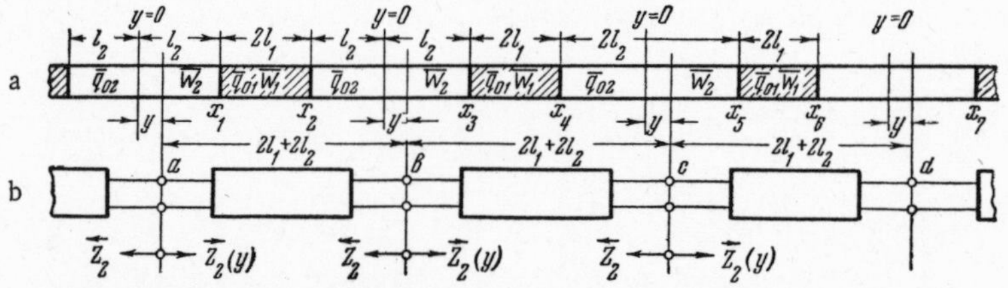

Fig. 16. An infinite periodically layered medium, where $2l_1 + 2l_2$ constitutes the period of the structure. a) A medium having two layers within the period of the structure; b) representation of above by a succession of equivalent two-terminal-pair networks, the network sections inserted on the basis of repetition of input impedances. $\bar{W}_1$, $\bar{q}_{01}$, and $2l_1$ are the parameters of the first layer, $\bar{W}_2$, $\bar{q}_{02}$, and $2l_2$ those of the second.

Statement of the Problem

To determine the wave characteristics of a periodically layered medium (Fig. 16a), we present it in the form of a series of four-pole networks (Fig. 16b), i.e., sections of length $2l_1 + 2l_2$, arbitrarily cut out of the path, where $2l_1$ is the thickness of the first layer; $2l_2$ is the thickness of the second layer, the coordinate y being considered as a variable quantity ranging from $-l$ to $+l$. With respect to the series of identical four-pole network equivalents obtained, we impose the condition of complete equivalence (for the entire range of frequencies) in its external work, i.e., complete equivalence of the oscillatory modes at points of contact between quadripoles to the oscillatory modes at corresponding points of the initial periodically layered medium.

From Fig. 16b, we see that, in the case $y=0$, the input impedances of the four-pole networks are mutually equal, $\vec{Z}_2(0) = \overleftarrow{Z}_2(0)$. Consequently, we have a sequence of balanced four-pole networks, connected up on the basis of impedance matching. In all remaining cases, where $y \neq 0$, the input impedances of the four-pole networks at points of contact between them are not equal,

$\vec{Z}_2(y) \neq \overleftarrow{Z}_2(y)$. However, input impedances of the same direction remain mutually equal. In the general case $(y \neq 0)$, we consequently end up with a series of four-pole networks series-connected on the basis of repetition of input terminal impedances [2, 4]. From the theory of four-pole networks, we know that the input impedances (iterative impedances [2]) of that type of four-pole networks have the following values, expressed in terms of the arm impedances of an equivalent mechanical four-pole network ($\bar{Z}_A$, $\bar{Z}_B$, $\bar{Z}_C$, see Fig. 17):

$$\left.\begin{aligned} \vec{Z}_2 &= \frac{1}{2}\left[\sqrt{(\bar{Z}_A+\bar{Z}_B)(\bar{Z}_A+\bar{Z}_B+4\bar{Z}_C)}+\bar{Z}_A-\bar{Z}_B\right]=f_1(p, y), \\ \overleftarrow{Z}_2 &= \frac{1}{2}\left[\sqrt{(\bar{Z}_A+\bar{Z}_B)(\bar{Z}_A+\bar{Z}_B+4\bar{Z}_C)}+\bar{Z}_B-\bar{Z}_A\right]=f_2(p, y), \end{aligned}\right\} \quad (170)$$

where $\bar{Z}_A$ and $\bar{Z}_B$ are the mechanical impedances of parallel arms of the four-pole network, $\bar{Z}_C$ is the mechanical impedance of the succeeding arm; $\bar{Z}_A$, $\bar{Z}_B$, $\bar{Z}_C$ are determined from formula (7).

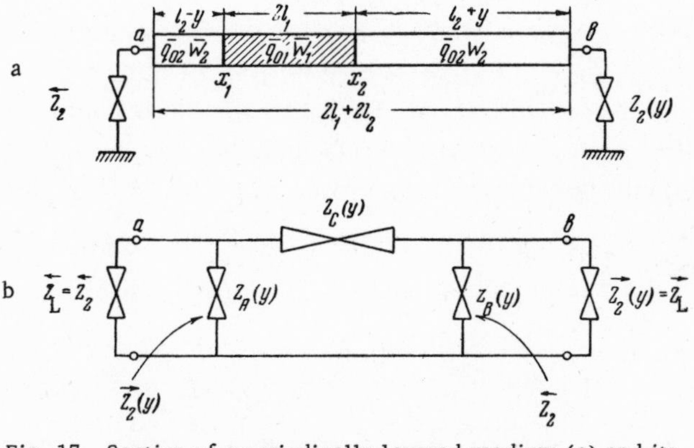

Fig. 17. Section of a periodically layered medium (a) and its representation by a Π-section mechanical four-pole network (b). $\vec{Z}_2(y) = \vec{Z}_L$ and $\overleftarrow{Z}_2 = \overleftarrow{Z}_L$ are the input impedances comprising the load impedances of the network section.

The sequence of steps in the solution of the problem may be presented as follows:

1. Determine the arm impedances $\bar{Z}_A$, $\bar{Z}_B$, $\bar{Z}_C$ of the equivalent four-pole network from open-circuit and short-circuit data (7);

2. Determine the input terminal impedances $\vec{Z}_2(y)$ and $\overleftarrow{Z}_2(y)$ of the four-pole networks with the aid of formulas (170);

3. Find the differential propagation constants in the second medium from (16) and (25), with the distribution of input impedances in the same medium, i.e., $\vec{Z}_2(y)$ and $\overleftarrow{Z}_2(y)$, known;

4. Determine the distribution of the input terminal impedances in the first medium (see Fig. 81, below), i.e., $\vec{Z}_1(u)$ and $\overleftarrow{Z}_1(u)$, by a simple substitution of subscripts *1* and *2* in the values found for $\vec{Z}_2(y)$ and $\overleftarrow{Z}_2(y)$, in the view of the symmetry of the problem relating to the first and second media. Having determined $\vec{Z}_1(u)$ and $\overleftarrow{Z}_1(u)$ as functions of the variable u, find the differential propagation constants for the first medium, with the aid of (16) and (25).

5. Find the integral wave characteristics for the first and second layers by using the method described above of integrating the differential propagation constants $\vec{D}_{\Gamma}$ and $\vec{D}_T$.

Determination of the Arm Impedances $\bar{Z}_A$, $\bar{Z}_B$, $\bar{Z}_C$ of an Equivalent Four-Terminal Network

We avail ourselves of (7) in order to determine the impedances of the arms of an equivalent four-pole network (Fig. 17b). For this purpose, we first determine the input impedances of a section of the medium, arbitrarily cut out (Fig. 17a), for the case of short-circuiting and open-circuiting of the opposing ends of the section.

The input impedance at point a with the terminals at point $в$ short-circuited (mechanical impedance equal to zero) is:

$$\bar{Z}_0^a = \overline{W}_2 \frac{\vec{Z}_0^{x_1} + \overline{W}_2 \operatorname{th} \bar{q}_{02}(l_2 - y)}{\vec{Z}_0^{x_1} \cdot \operatorname{th} \bar{q}_{02}(l_2 - y) + \overline{W}_2}, \tag{171}$$

where $\vec{Z}_0^{x_1}$ is the input impedance at point x_1, which is determined in harmony with the rule laid down in section 2:

$$\vec{Z}_0^{x_1} = \frac{\overline{W}_1 \overline{W}_2 \operatorname{cth} \bar{q}_{01} 2l \cdot \operatorname{th} \bar{q}_{02}(l_2 + y) + \overline{W}_1^2}{\overline{W}_1 \operatorname{cth} \bar{q}_{01} 2l_1 + W_2 \operatorname{th} \bar{q}_{02}(l_2 + y)}. \tag{172}$$

The input impedance at point a, in the open-circuited case (mechanical impedance equal to infinity) across point $в$ is:

$$\bar{Z}_\infty^a = \overline{W}_2 \frac{\vec{Z}_\infty^{x_1} + \overline{W}_2 \operatorname{th} \bar{q}_{02}(l - y)}{\vec{Z}_\infty^{x_1} \operatorname{th} \bar{q}_{02}(l - y) + \overline{W}_2}, \tag{173}$$

where $\vec{Z}_{\infty}^{x_1}$ is the input impedance at point x_1:

$$\vec{Z}_{\infty}^{x_1}=\frac{\bar{W}_1\bar{W}_2 \operatorname{cth}\bar{q}_{01}2l_1\cdot\operatorname{cth}\bar{q}_{02}(l_2+y)+\bar{W}_1^2}{\bar{W}_1\operatorname{cth}\bar{q}_{01}2l_1+\bar{W}_2\operatorname{cth}\bar{q}_{02}(l_2+y)}. \tag{174}$$

A similar approach yields the input impedances at point $\textit{в}$ in the case of a short-circuit across opposing terminals, i.e., at point a.

$$\bar{Z}_0^b=\bar{W}_2\frac{\overleftarrow{Z}_0^{x_2}+\bar{W}_2\operatorname{th}\bar{q}_{02}(l_2+y)}{\overleftarrow{Z}_0^{x_2}\operatorname{th}\bar{q}_{02}\cdot(l_2+y)+\bar{W}_2}, \tag{175}$$

where $\overleftarrow{Z}_0^{x_2}$ is the input impedance at point x_2, and is determined from the equation

$$\overleftarrow{Z}_0^{x_2}=\frac{\bar{W}_1\bar{W}_2\operatorname{cth}\bar{q}_{01}2l_1\operatorname{th}\bar{q}_{02}(l_2-y)+\bar{W}_1^2}{\bar{W}_1\operatorname{cth}\bar{q}_{01}2l_1+\bar{W}_2\operatorname{th}\bar{q}_{02}(l_2-y)}. \tag{176}$$

The input impedance at point $\textit{в}$ in the case of an open-circuit across terminals a is:

$$\bar{Z}_{\infty}^{в}=\bar{W}_2\frac{\overleftarrow{Z}_{\infty}^{x_2}+\bar{W}_2\cdot\operatorname{th}\bar{q}_{02}(l_2+y)}{\overleftarrow{Z}_{\infty}^{x_2}\cdot\operatorname{th}\bar{q}_{02}\cdot(l_2+y)+\bar{W}_2}, \tag{177}$$

where $\overleftarrow{Z}_{\infty}^{x_2}$ is the input impedance at point x_2:

$$\overleftarrow{Z}_{\infty}^{x_2}=\frac{\bar{W}_1\bar{W}_2\operatorname{cth}\bar{q}_{01}2l_1\operatorname{cth}\bar{q}_{02}(l_2-y)+\bar{W}_1^2}{\bar{W}_1\operatorname{cth}\bar{q}_{01}2l_1+\bar{W}_2\operatorname{cth}\bar{q}_{02}(l_2-y)}. \tag{178}$$

Finally, we rewrite (7) in our notation:

$$\left.\begin{aligned}\bar{Z}_C&=\sqrt{\bar{Z}_{\infty}^{в}\left(\bar{Z}_{\infty}^{a}-\bar{Z}_0^{a}\right)},\\ \bar{Z}_A&=\bar{Z}_{\infty}^{a}-\sqrt{\bar{Z}_{\infty}^{в}\cdot\left(\bar{Z}_{\infty}^{a}-\bar{Z}_0^{a}\right)},\\ \bar{Z}_B&=\bar{Z}_{\infty}^{в}-\sqrt{\bar{Z}_{\infty}^{в}\cdot\left(\bar{Z}_{\infty}^{a}-\bar{Z}_0^{a}\right)}.\end{aligned}\right\} \tag{179}$$

Substituting here the values of the input impedances (171), (173), (177), we obtain, after some algebra, the impedances of the arms of the equivalent four-pole network (cf. Fig. 17b):

$$\begin{aligned}\bar{Z}_C&=\frac{\sqrt{[Z_0 2l_1-Z_{\infty}2l_1][Z_0(l_2+y)-Z_{\infty}(l_2+y)][Z_{\infty}(l_2-y)-Z_0(l_2-y)]}}{Z_{\infty}(l_2+y)[Z_{\infty}2l_1+Z_{\infty}(l_2-y)]+Z_{\infty}2l_1[Z_{\infty}(l_2-y)+Z_0(2l_1)]}\times\\ &\qquad\times\sqrt{Z_{\infty}(l_2+y)\cdot Z_{\infty}(l_2-y)\cdot Z_{\infty}2l_1};\\ \bar{Z}_A&=\bar{Z}_{\infty}(l_2-y)\frac{Z_{\infty}2l_1[Z_{\infty}(l_2+y)+Z_0 2l_1]+Z_0(l_2-y)[Z_{\infty}2l_1+Z_{\infty}(l_2+y)]}{Z_{\infty}(l_2+y)[Z_{\infty}2l_1+Z_{\infty}(l_2-y)]+Z_{\infty}2l_1[Z_{\infty}(l_2-y)+Z_0 2l_1]}-\bar{Z}_C;\\ \bar{Z}_B&=\bar{Z}_{\infty}(l_2+y)\frac{Z_{\infty}2l_1[Z_{\infty}(l_2-y)+Z_0 2l_1]+Z_0(l_2+y)[Z_{\infty}2l_1+Z_{\infty}(l_2-y)]}{Z_{\infty}(l_2+y)[Z_{\infty}2l_1+Z_{\infty}(l_2-y)]+Z_{\infty}2l_1[Z_{\infty}(l_2-y)+Z_0 2l_1]}-\bar{Z}_C,\end{aligned} \tag{180}$$

where we have, by definition:

$$
\left.
\begin{aligned}
&Z_0 2l_1 = \overline{W}_1 \operatorname{th} \bar{q}_{01} 2l_1; \; Z_0 (l_2 + y) = \overline{W}_2 \operatorname{th} \bar{q}_{02} (l_2 + y);\\
&Z_0 (l_2 - y) = \overline{W}_2 \operatorname{th} \bar{q}_{02} (l_2 - y); \; Z_\infty 2l_1 = \overline{W}_1 \operatorname{cth} \bar{q}_{01} 2l_1;\\
&Z_\infty (l_2 + y) = \overline{W}_2 \operatorname{cth} \bar{q}_{02} (l_2 + y); \; Z_\infty (l_2 - y) = \overline{W}_2 \operatorname{cth} \bar{q}_{02} (l_2 - y).
\end{aligned}
\right\} \tag{181}
$$

The impedances of the arms of the equivalent four-pole network $\bar{Z}_A$, $\bar{Z}_B$, $\bar{Z}_C$ are of independent interest in research on the physics of elastic waves, e.g., for the determination of the nature of the arm impedances (whether inertial, elastic, resistive) for different frequencies.

Determination of the Input Impedances of a Periodically Layered Medium

The input impedances for the second medium are determined on the basis of (170), into which the values found for $\bar{Z}_A$, $\bar{Z}_B$, $\bar{Z}_C$ are substituted. Carrying through the substitution and omitting transformations, we arrive at the values of the input impedances $\vec{Z}_2(y)$ in the second medium for a wave advancing from left to right:

$$
\vec{Z}_2(y) = \frac{\sqrt{1 + \dfrac{4\left(\overline{W}_2^2 - Z_\infty^2 2l_1\right)\left[\overline{W}_2^2 - Z_\infty^2 (l_2 + y)\right]\left[\overline{W}_2^2 - Z_\infty (l_2 - y)\right]}{\left\{2\left[\overline{W}_2^2 + Z_\infty (l_2 + y) \cdot Z_\infty (l_2 - y)\right] Z_\infty 2l_1 + \left(W_1^2 + \overline{W}_2^2\right)\left[Z_\infty (l_2 + y) + Z_\infty (l_2 - y)\right]\right\}^2}}}{\dfrac{2\left\{Z_\infty 2l_1 \left[Z_\infty (l_2 + y) + Z_\infty (l_2 - y)\right] + Z_\infty (l_2 + y) \cdot Z_\infty (l_2 - y) + \overline{W}_1^2\right\}}{\left[2\overline{W}_2^2 + Z_\infty (l_2 + y) \cdot Z_\infty (l_2 - y)\right] Z_\infty 2l_1 + \left(\overline{W}_1^2 + W_2^2\right)\left[Z_\infty (l_2 + y) + Z_\infty (l_2 - y)\right]}} +
$$

$$
+ \frac{\left[Z_\infty (l_2 + y) - Z_\infty (l_2 - y)\right]\left(\overline{W}_2^2 - \overline{W}_1^2\right)}{2\left\{Z_\infty 2l_1 \left[Z_\infty (l_2 + y) + Z_\infty (l_2 - y)\right] + Z_\infty (l_2 + y) \cdot Z_\infty (l_2 - y) + \overline{W}_1^2\right\}}. \tag{182}
$$

In transforming the hyperbolic functions to arguments $\bar{q}_{01} \cdot l$ and $\bar{q}_{02} \cdot l$, we get, after transformations:

$$
\vec{Z}_2(y) = \overline{W}_2 \frac{A_2 - \operatorname{sh} 2\bar{q}_{02} y}{B_2 - \operatorname{ch} 2\bar{q}_{02} y} \bigg|_{-l_2 < y < +l_2}, \tag{183}
$$

where we have, by definition:

$$
\left.
\begin{aligned}
A_2 = {} & \frac{2\sqrt{\left(\overline{W}_1 \operatorname{th} \bar{q}_{01} l_1 \operatorname{th} \bar{q}_{02} l_2 + \overline{W}_2\right)\left(\overline{W}_2 \operatorname{th} \bar{q}_{01} l_1 \operatorname{th} \bar{q}_{02} l_2 + \overline{W}_1\right)}}{\left(\overline{W}_2^2 - \overline{W}_1^2\right) \operatorname{th} \bar{q}_{01} l_1 \left(\operatorname{th}^2 \bar{q}_{02} l_2 - 1\right)} \times \\
& \times \sqrt{\left(\overline{W}_1 \operatorname{th} \bar{q}_{01} l_1 + \overline{W}_2 \operatorname{th} q_{02} l_2\right)\left(\overline{W}_1 \operatorname{th} q_{02} l_2 + \overline{W}_1 \operatorname{th} \bar{q}_{01} l_1\right)}; \\
B_2 = {} & \frac{2\left(\overline{W}_2 + \overline{W}_1 \operatorname{th} \bar{q}_{01} l_1 \operatorname{th} \bar{q}_{02} l_2\right)\left(\overline{W}_1 \operatorname{th} \bar{q}_{02} l_2 + \overline{W}_2 \operatorname{th} \bar{q}_{01} l_1\right)}{\left(\overline{W}_2^2 - \overline{W}_1^2\right) \operatorname{th} \bar{q}_{01} l_1 \left(\operatorname{th}^2 \bar{q}_{02} l_2 - 1\right)} + 1.
\end{aligned}
\right\} \tag{184}
$$

The quantities A_2 and B_2 are interrelated by the equation $A_2^2 = B_2^2 - 1$.

The input impedance $\vec{Z}_1$ for the first layer may be determined in the same layer as the impedance for the second layer. However, due to the symmetry of the problem relating to the first and second layers, the input impedance $\vec{Z}_1(u)$ for layer *1* may be written

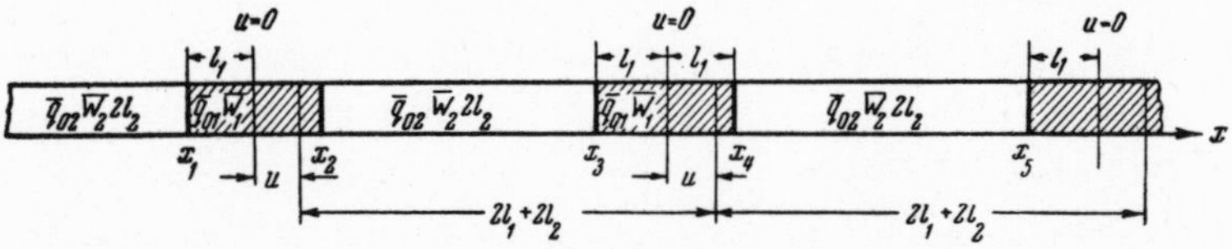

Fig. 18. Representation of an infinite periodically structured layer composed of sections including the complete second layer.

by substituting into (183) subscripts *1* and *2* [whereupon the new variable u (cf. Fig. 18) counted off from the middle of layer *1* is used in place of the variable y; the variable u ranges from $-l_1$ to $+l_1$]:

$$\vec{Z}_1(u) = \overline{W}_1 \frac{A_1 - \operatorname{sh} 2\bar{q}_{01}u}{B_1 - \operatorname{ch} 2q_{01}u}\Bigg|_{-l_1<u<+l_1}, \tag{185}$$

where we have, by definition:

$$\left.\begin{aligned} A &= \frac{2\sqrt{(\overline{W}_2 \operatorname{th} \bar{q}_{02}l_2 \cdot \operatorname{th} \bar{q}_{01}l_1 + \overline{W}_1)(\overline{W}_1 \operatorname{th} \bar{q}_{02}l_2 \operatorname{th} \bar{q}_{01}l_1 + \overline{W}_2)}}{(\overline{W}_1^2 - \overline{W}_2^2) \operatorname{th} q_{02}l_2 (\operatorname{th}^2 \bar{q}_{01}l_1 - 1)} \times \\ &\qquad \times \sqrt{(\overline{W}_2 \operatorname{th} \bar{q}_{02}l_2 + \overline{W}_1 \operatorname{th} \bar{q}_{01}l_1)(\overline{W}_2 \operatorname{th} \bar{q}_{01}l_1 + \overline{W}_1 \operatorname{th} \bar{q}_{02}l_2)}; \\ B_1 &= \frac{2(\overline{W}_1 + \overline{W}_2 \operatorname{th} \bar{q}_{02}l_2 \cdot \operatorname{th} \bar{q}_{01}l_1)(\overline{W}_2 \operatorname{th} \bar{q}_{01}l_1 + \overline{W}_1 \operatorname{th} \bar{q}_{02}l_2)}{(\overline{W}_1^2 - \overline{W}_2^2) \operatorname{th} \bar{q}_{02}l_2 (\operatorname{th}^2 q_{01}l_1 - 1)} + 1, \end{aligned}\right\} \tag{186}$$

and the equation $A_1^2 = B_1^2 - 1$ holds.

The values obtained for the input impedances $\vec{Z}_2(y)$ and $\vec{Z}_1(u)$ enable us, finally, to determine the differential propagation constants in layers *1* and *2* for velocity and pressure waves.

Determination of $\vec{D}_V$ and $\vec{D}_T$ in a Periodically Layered Medium

We avail ourselves of (16) and (15) in order to determine the differential propagation constants of velocity and pressure waves in the first medium:

$$\left.\begin{aligned}\vec{D}_{1V} &= \frac{\bar{Z}_1(u)}{\overline{W}_1}\bar{q}_{01} = \bar{q}_{01}\frac{A_1 - \text{sh}\,2\bar{q}_{01}u}{B_1 - \text{ch}\,2\bar{q}_{01}u} = f_{1V}(u, p),\\ \vec{D}_{1T} &= \frac{\overline{W}_1}{\bar{Z}_1(u)}\bar{q}_{01} = \bar{q}_{01}\frac{B_1 - \text{ch}\,2\bar{q}_{01}u}{A_1 - \text{sh}\,2\bar{q}_{01}u} = f_{1T}(u, p)\end{aligned}\right\} \tag{187}$$

and in the second medium:

$$\left.\begin{aligned}\vec{D}_{2V} &= \frac{\bar{Z}_2(y)}{\overline{W}_2}\bar{q}_{02} = \bar{q}_{02}\frac{A_2 - \text{sh}\,2\bar{q}_{02}y}{B_2 - \text{ch}\,2\bar{q}_{02}y} = f_{2V}(y, p),\\ \vec{D}_{2T} &= \frac{\overline{W}_2}{\bar{Z}_2(y)}\bar{q}_{02} = \bar{q}_{02}\frac{B_2 - \text{ch}\,2\bar{q}_{02}y}{A_2 - \text{sh}\,2\bar{q}_{02}y} = f_{2T}(y, p),\end{aligned}\right\} \tag{188}$$

where the definitions of A_1, B_1, A_2 and B_2 are indicated in (184) and (186). Having utilized (187) and (188) and also (26), we now determine the differential propagation constants of an intensity wave for the first medium:

$$\vec{D}_{1Q} = \frac{1}{2}(\vec{D}_{1V} + \vec{D}_{1T}) = \frac{\bar{q}_{01}}{2}\cdot\frac{(A_1 - \text{ch}\,2\bar{q}_{01}u)^2 + (B_1 - \text{ch}\,2\bar{q}_{01}u)^2}{(B_1 - \text{sh}\,2q_{01}u)(A_1 - \text{sh}\,2\bar{q}_{01}u)} = f_{1Q}(u, p) \tag{189}$$

and for the second medium:

$$\vec{D}_{2Q} = \frac{1}{2}(\vec{D}_{2V} + \vec{D}_{2T}) = \frac{\bar{q}_{02}}{2}\cdot\frac{(A_2 - \text{sh}\,2\bar{q}_{02}y)^2 + (B_2 - \text{ch}\,2\bar{q}_{02}y)^2}{(B_2 - \text{ch}\,2\bar{q}_{02}y)(A_2 - \text{sh}\,2\bar{q}_{02}y)} = f_{2Q}(u, p). \tag{189}$$

In the case of a steady-state mode of oscillations ($p = i\omega$) in a periodically layered medium, (187) and (188) are rewritten in the following form ($\bar{q}_{01} = ik_1$; $\bar{q}_{02} = ik_2$):

$$\left.\begin{aligned}\vec{D}_{1V} &= ik_1\frac{A_1 - i\sin 2k_1u}{B_1 - \cos 2k_1u} = f_{1V}(u, \omega),\\ \vec{D}_{2V} &= ik_2\frac{A_2 - i\sin 2k_2y}{B_2 - \cos 2k_2y} = f_{2V}(y, \omega),\\ \vec{D}_{1T} &= ik_1\frac{B_1 - \cos 2k_1u}{A_1 - i\sin 2k_1u} = f_{1T}(u, \omega),\\ \vec{D}_{2T} &= ik_2\frac{B_2 - \cos 2k_2y}{A_2 - i\sin 2k_2y} = f_{2T}(y, \omega),\end{aligned}\right\} \tag{190}$$

and the quantities A_1; B_1; A_2; B_2 will be equal to:

$$\left.\begin{aligned}A_2 &= \frac{\pm 2\sqrt{(W_2 - W_1\,\text{tg}\,k_1l_1\,\text{tg}\,k_2l_2)(W_1 - W_2\,\text{tg}\,k_1l_1\,\text{tg}\,k_2l_2)}}{(W_1^2 - W_2^2)\,\text{tg}\,k_1l_1(1 + \text{tg}^2k_2l_2)}\times\\ &\quad\times\sqrt{(W_1\,\text{tg}\,k_1l_1 + W_2\,\text{tg}\,k_2l_2)(W_1\,\text{tg}\,k_2l_2 + W_2\,\text{tg}\,k_1l_1)},\\ B_2 &= \frac{2(W_2 - W_1\,\text{tg}\,k_1l_1\,\text{tg}\,k_2l_2)(W_1\,\text{tg}\,k_2l_2 + W_2\,\text{tg}\,k_1l_1)}{(W_1^2 - W_2^2)\,\text{tg}\,k_1l_1(1 + \text{tg}^2k_2l_2)} + 1,\end{aligned}\right\} \tag{191}$$

$$\left.\begin{aligned} A_1 &= \frac{\pm 2\sqrt{(W_1 - W_2 \operatorname{tg} k_1 l_1 \operatorname{tg} k_2 l_2)(W_2 - W_1 \operatorname{tg} k_1 l_1 \operatorname{tg} k_2 l_2)}}{(W_2^2 - W_1^2) \operatorname{tg} k_2 l_2 (1 + \operatorname{tg}^2 k_1 l_1)} \times \\ &\quad \times \sqrt{(W_2 \operatorname{tg} k_2 l_2 + W_1 \operatorname{tg} k_1 l_1)(W_2 \operatorname{tg} k_1 l_1 + W_1 \operatorname{tg} k_2 l_2)}, \\ B_1 &= \frac{2(W_1 - W_2 \operatorname{tg} k_1 l_1 \cdot \operatorname{tg} k_2 l_2)(W_2 \operatorname{tg} k_1 l_1 + W_1 \operatorname{tg} k_2 l_2)}{(W_2^2 - W_1^2) \operatorname{tg} k_2 l_2 (1 + \operatorname{tg}^2 k_1 l_1)} + 1, \end{aligned}\right\} \quad (192)$$

where they will be related by the equations $A_2^2 = B_2^2 - 1$; $A_1^2 = B_1^2 - 1$.

Consider several particular cases of passage of sinusoidal waves through a periodically layered medium:

1. Suppose that the frequency $\omega \to 0$. This corresponds to that case where the resultant wave is propagating through a periodically layered medium (Fig. 16) at a wavelength $\lambda_p \gg 2l_1 + 2l_2$. The differential propagation constants in the first and second medium (190) take on the following values (we here neglect second order terms):

$$\left.\begin{aligned} \vec{D}_{1V} &= i\frac{\omega}{c_1}\sqrt{\frac{W_2(W_1\tau_1 + W_2\tau_2)}{W_1(W_2\tau_1 + W_1\tau_2)}} = 0 + i\beta'_{1V}; \\ \vec{D}_{1T} &= i\frac{\omega}{c_1}\sqrt{\frac{W_1(W_2\tau_1 + W_1\tau_2)}{W_2(W_1\tau_1 + W_2\tau_2)}} = 0 + i\beta'_{1T}; \\ \vec{D}_{2V} &= i\frac{\omega}{c_2}\sqrt{\frac{W_1}{W_2}\cdot\frac{(W_1\tau_1 + W_2\tau_2)}{(W_1\tau_2 + W_2\tau_1)}} = 0 + i\beta'_{2V}; \\ \vec{D}_{2T} &= i\frac{\omega}{c_2}\sqrt{\frac{W_2}{W_1}\cdot\frac{(W_1\tau_2 + W_2\tau_1)}{(W_1\tau_1 + W_2\tau_2)}} = 0 + i\beta'_{2T}, \end{aligned}\right\} \quad (193)$$

where we define: $\tau_1 = \frac{l_1}{c_1}$; $\tau_2 = \frac{l_2}{c_2}$.

The differential propagation constants are, with an accuracy to the magnitude of the second order of smallness, independent in the case at hand of the variables u and y, and accordingly have a constant magnitude within the corresponding layers. In addition, in view of the fact that the differential attenuation constants α'_V and α'_T vanish, we arrive at the conclusion that the amplitudes of the $\bar{V}$ and $\bar{T}$ waves are constant within the separate layers.

We now determine the differential velocities of propagation of velocity waves $\bar{V}$ and pressure waves $\bar{T}$. For this purpose, we make use of the equation $c' = \frac{\omega}{\beta'}$. Substituting into this equation the values of the differential phase constants β' (193), we then find the differential velocities of $\bar{V}$ and $\bar{T}$ waves in the corresponding layers of the periodically layered medium:

$$\left.\begin{aligned} c'_{1V} &= c_1\sqrt{\frac{W_1(W_2\tau_1+W_1\tau_2)}{W_2(W_1\tau_1+W_2\tau_2)}};\ c'_{1T}=c_1\sqrt{\frac{W_2(W_1\tau_1+W_2\tau_2)}{W_1(W_2\tau_1+W_1\tau_2)}};\\ c'_{2V} &= c_2\sqrt{\frac{W_2(W_1\tau_2+W_2\tau_1)}{W_1(W_1\tau_1+W_2\tau_2)}};\ c'_{2T}=c_2\sqrt{\frac{W_1(W_1\tau_1+W_2\tau_2)}{W_2(W_1\tau_2+W_2\tau_1)}};\end{aligned}\right\} \qquad (194)$$

and, accordingly, within each layer the differential velocities are constant quantities, dependent on the relationship between the wave impedances W_1 and W_2, and also dependent on the time taken for a homogeneous wave to traverse the first layer, i.e., $\tau_1 = \frac{l_1}{c_1}$ and, the second layer, i.e., $\tau_2 = \frac{l_2}{c_2}$.

We have still to write out the values of the differential velocities for the intensity wave $\overline{Q}$ [we obtain this from (193)], with (189) available:

$$\left.\begin{aligned} c'_{1Q} &= \frac{2c_1\sqrt{W_1W_2(W_1\tau_1+W_2\tau_2)(W_1\tau_2+W_2\tau_1)}}{2W_1W_2\tau_1+(W_1^2+W_2^2)\tau_2},\\ c'_{2Q} &= \frac{2c_2\sqrt{W_1W_2(W_1\tau_1+W_2\tau_2)(W_1\tau_2+W_2\tau_1)}}{2W_1W_2\tau_2+(W_1^2+W_2^2)\tau_1},\end{aligned}\right\} \qquad (195)$$

where c'_{1Q} is the velocity of an intensity wave $\overline{Q}$ in layer *1*, and c'_{2Q} is the velocity of a $\overline{Q}$ wave in layer *2*. We shall return later to these formulas for the velocities in layers of a periodically layered medium when we take up the integral wave properties. However, let us note the following at this point. In the case considered here, $\omega \to 0$ and we have in the periodically layered medium not a homogeneous wave, but a resultant wave, comprising in each layer the sum of multiple superpositions of waves reflected from the interfaces in the periodically layered wave, and direct forward-going waves.

In the first approximation, (194) and (195) obtained above retain their validity for a wave impulse propagating through a periodically layered medium, but the basic wavelength is $\lambda \gg 2l_1 + 2l_2$.

Figure 19 shows the distribution of the differential velocities in a periodically layered medium, plotted on the basis of the formulas obtained, when $\omega \to 0$. We assume $\tau_1 = \tau_2$; $W_1 = 2W_2$; $c_2 = 2c_1$.

2. Consider the particular case where $\operatorname{tg} k_1l_1 \to \pm\infty$ or $k_1l_1 = \frac{\pi n}{2}$, which corresponds to the equation $2l_1 = \frac{\lambda_1}{2}n$, where $n = 1, 3, 5, 7, \ldots$ i.e., the first layer accommodates a multiple of half wave-

lengths. In that case, the expressions for differential propagation constants for the first medium will be greatly simplified, assuming the following form:

$$\left.\begin{aligned}
\vec{D}_{1V} &= \frac{k_1 \sin 2k_1u}{\dfrac{W_1^2+W_2^2}{W_1^2-W_2^2} - \cos 2k_1u} + \\
&\quad + i\,\frac{k_1 2W_1W_2}{W_1^2+W_2^2-(W_1^2-W_2^2)\cdot\cos 2k_1u} = \alpha'_{1V}+\beta'_{1V},\\
\vec{D}_{1T} &= \frac{k_1 \sin 2k_1u\left(\cos 2k_1u - \dfrac{W_1^2+W_2^2}{W_1^2-W_2^2}\right)}{\dfrac{4W_1^2\cdot W_2^2}{(W_1^2-W_2^2)^2}+\sin^2 2k_1u} + \\
&\quad + i\,\frac{k_1\left(\dfrac{W_1^2+W_2^2}{W_1^2-W_2^2} - \cos 2k_1u\right)}{\dfrac{2W_1W_2}{W_1^2-W_2^2}+\dfrac{W_1^2-W_2^2}{2W_1W_2}\cdot\sin^2 2k_1u} = \alpha'_{1T}+i\beta'_{1T}.
\end{aligned}\right\} \quad (196)$$

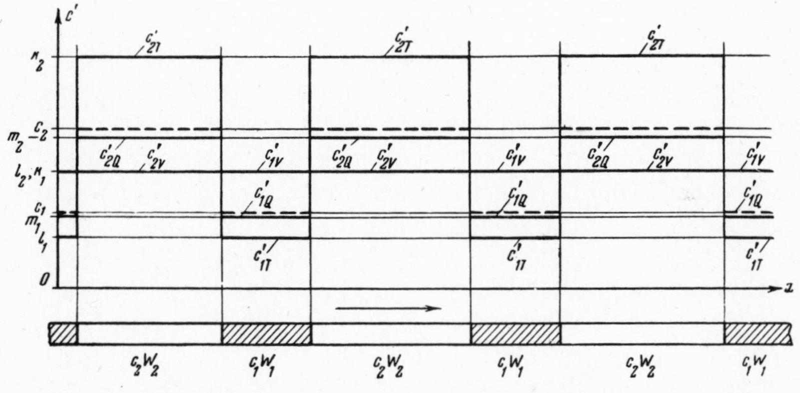

Fig. 19. Distribution of the differential propagation constants c' in an infinite periodically layered medium, when $\omega \to 0$. It is assumed that $\tau_1 = \tau_2$ i. e., $\frac{l_1}{c_1} = \frac{l_2}{c_2}$; $W_1 = 2W_2$; $c_2 = 2c_1$. The points laid off along the ordinate correspond to the following values of c': $k_1 = c_1\sqrt{\frac{W_1}{W_2}}$; $l_1 = c_1\sqrt{\frac{W_2}{W_1}}$; $m_1 = c_1\frac{2\sqrt{W_1W_2}}{W_1+W_2}$; $k_2 = c_2\sqrt{\frac{W_1}{W_2}}$; $l_2 = c_2\sqrt{\frac{W_2}{W_1}}$; $m_2 = c_2\frac{2\sqrt{W_1W_2}}{W_1+W_2}$.

The origin of the coordinates for u is situated in the middle of the first layer. We now transform the coordinates in such a manner that the origin of the frame of reference falls on the interface between the layers (as was the case earlier in sections 3 and 4). If the origin of the frame of reference of the new coordinate x is placed at the right boundary of the first layer, then we have the relationship $u = x + l_1$. Replacing in (196) the instantaneous coordinate u by the new coordinate x we obtain, as a result:

$$\left.\begin{aligned}
\vec{D}_{1V} &= \frac{k_1 \dfrac{W_2^2 - W_1^2}{W_2^2 + W_1^2} \sin 2k_1 x}{1 + \dfrac{-W_2^2 + W_1^2}{W_2^2 + W_1^2} \cdot \cos 2k_1 x} + i \frac{2 \dfrac{k_1 W_1 W_2}{W_1^2 + W_2^2}}{1 + \dfrac{-W_2^2 + W_1^2}{W_2^2 + W_1^2} \cdot \cos 2k_1 x} = \alpha_{1V} + i\beta'_{1V}; \\
\vec{D}_{1T} &= \frac{k_1 \dfrac{W_1^2 - W_2^2}{W_1^2 + W_2^2} \cdot \sin 2k_1 x}{1 + \dfrac{-W_1^2 + W_2^2}{W_2^2 + W_1^2} \cos 2k_1 x} + i \frac{2 \dfrac{k_1 W_1 W_2}{W_1^2 + W_2^2}}{1 + \dfrac{-W_1^2 + W_2^2}{W_1^2 + W_2^2} \cdot \cos 2k_1 x} = \alpha'_{1T} + i\beta'_{1T},
\end{aligned}\right\} \quad (197)$$

where we make use of the equations: $\sin 2k_1 u = -\sin 2k_1 x$; $\cos 2k_1 u = -\cos 2k_1 x$ assuming, according to the condition stipulated, that $\cos 2k_1 l_1 = -1$; $\sin 2k_1 l_1 = 0$.

Comparing the values obtained for the differential constants (197) for the first layer with the similar constants (74) obtained in the case of a single interface (cf. section 3), we arrive at the conclusion that the distribution of differential velocities c' and differential attenuation constants α' for $\bar{V}$ and $\bar{T}$ waves in the first layer of a periodically layered medium is similar to the distribution of c' and α' in the first medium (Fig. 5). In addition, we note that the differential constants (197) are independent of the value of $\mathrm{tg}\ k_2 l_2$, which attests, in the case in question, to the arbitrary character of the wavelength relation in the second layer to the layer thickness, i.e., $\frac{\lambda_2}{2l_2}$;

The differential propagation constants (190) in the second layer, in the case in question, $\mathrm{tg}\, k_1 l_1 \rightarrow \pm\infty$, take on the following values:

$$\vec{D}_{2V}\, 0+ik_2; \quad \vec{D}_{2T}=0+ik_2 \tag{198}$$

and, consequently, $\bar{V}$, $\bar{T}$ and $\bar{Q}$ waves propagate in the second layer from point to point in the layer without altering the velocity of propagation or the wave amplitudes, i.e., a homogeneous wave exists in the second layer.

This result was only to be expected, since it was shown (cf. section 4, and Fig. 13) that the layer in which a half wavelength is accommodated, and which is sandwiched between identical media, completely transmits (without reflections) a steady-state sinusoidal wave.

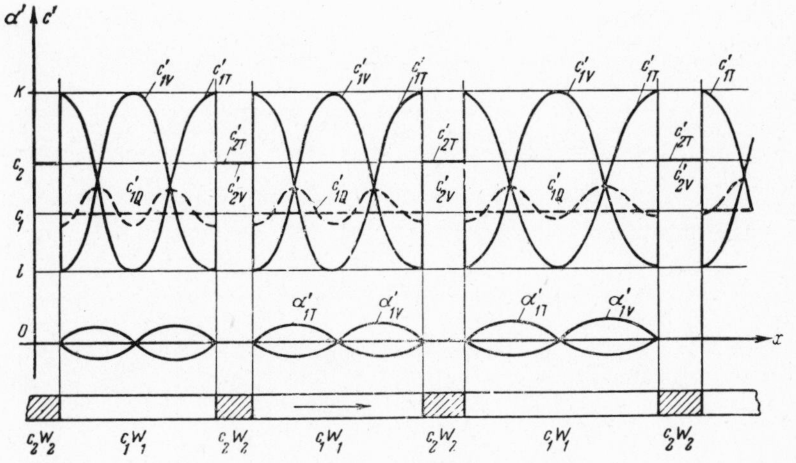

Fig. 20. Distribution of differential velocities of propagation c' and of attenuation constants α' of $\bar{V}$ and $\bar{T}$ waves in a periodically layered medium, when layer 1 accomodates half wavelengths of a homogeneous wave $2l_1=\frac{\lambda_1}{2}$. The relationship between $2l_2$ and λ_2 in the second layer is arbitrary in this case. We assume $W_2 = 2W_1$ Points laid off on the ordinate correspond to the following values of c':

$$k=c_1\frac{W_2}{W_1}; \quad l=c_1\frac{W_1}{W_2}$$

The distribution of c' and α' in a periodically layered medium, in the case $\operatorname{tg} k_1 l_1 \rightarrow \pm\infty$, is presented in Fig. 20; the graphs are based on (197) and (198), for $W_2 = 2W_1$.

It may be shown that a similar phenomenon will occur in the case where a multiple number of waves, i.e., $2l = \lambda_1 n$, where $n = 1, 2, 3, \ldots$ is accommodated in the first layer of a periodically layered medium.

3. Put $\operatorname{tg} k_1 l_1 = \operatorname{tg} k_2 l_2 = \sqrt{3}$, which corresponds to the equations $\frac{\lambda_1}{2l_1} = 3$; $\frac{\lambda_1}{2l_2} = 3$. Equations (191) and (192) in that case assume the form[1]:

$$A_2 = \frac{-\sqrt{(W_2 - 3W_1)(W_1 - 3W_2)}}{2(W_1 - W_2)}; \quad A_1 = \frac{-\sqrt{(W_1 - 3W_2)(W_2 - 3W_1)}}{2(W_2 - W_1)}; \tag{199}$$

$$B_2 = -\frac{W_1 + W_2}{2(W_1 - W_2)}; \quad B_1 = \frac{-(W_1 + W_2)}{2(W_2 - W_1)}, \tag{200}$$

and the differential propagation constants (190) for the second layer assume the form:

$$\vec{D}_{2V} = ik_2 \frac{\sqrt{(W_2 - 3W_1)(W_1 - 3W_2)} + 2i(W_1 - W_2) \cdot \sin 2k_2 y}{(W_1 + W_2) + 2(W_1 - W_2) \cdot \cos 2k_2 y}, \tag{201}$$

$$\vec{D}_{2T} = ik_2 \frac{(W_1 + W_2) + 2(W_1 - W_2)\cos 2k_2 y}{\sqrt{(W_2 - 3W_1)(W_1 - 3W_2)} + 2i(W_1 - W_2)\sin 2k_2 y}. \tag{202}$$

Solving $\vec{D}_{2V}$ and $\vec{D}_{2T}$ with respect to real and imaginary parts, and then determining the differential velocities, we have:

$$\left.\begin{aligned} c'_{2V} &= c_2 \frac{n_{12} + 1 + 2(n_{12} - 1)\cos 2k_2 y}{\sqrt{(1 - 3n_{12})(n_{12} - 3)}}, \\ c'_{2T} &= c_2 \frac{n_{12} + 1 - 2(n_{12} - 1)\cos 2k_2 y}{\sqrt{(1 - 3n_{12})(n_{12} - 3)}}, \\ \alpha'_{2V} &= \frac{2k_2(1 - n_{12})\sin 2k_2 y}{(n_{12} + 1) + 2(n_{12} - 1)\cos 2k_2 y}, \\ \alpha'_{2T} &= \frac{2k_2(n_{12} - 1)\sin 2k_2 y}{(n_{12} + 1) - 2(n_{12} - 1)\cos 2k_2 y}, \end{aligned}\right\} \tag{203}$$

where we define $n_{12} = \frac{W_1}{W_2}$. Similarly, we now find the differential velocities c'_1 and the differential attenuation constants a'_1 in the first layer:

[1] The minus sign is taken before the root, which leads us, in the case $W_1 = W_2$, to the familiar result.

$$\left.\begin{aligned} c'_{1V} &= c_1 \frac{n_{21}+1+2(n_{21}-1)\cos 2k_1u}{\sqrt{(1-3n_{21})(n_{21}-3)}}, \\ c'_{1T} &= c_1 \frac{n_{21}+1-(2n_{21}-1)\cos 2k_1u}{\sqrt{(1-3n_{21})(n_{21}-3)}}, \\ \alpha'_{1V} &= \frac{2k_1(1-n_{21})\sin 2k_1u}{(n_{21}+1)+2(n_{21}-1)\cos 2k_1u}, \\ \alpha'_{1T} &= \frac{2k_1(n_{21}-1)\sin 2k_1u}{(n_{21}+1)-2(n_{21}-1)\cos 2k_1u}, \end{aligned}\right\} \qquad (204)$$

where we define $n_{21}=\frac{W_2}{W_1}$. Finally, the values of the differential velocities of the intensity wave, for the first and second layers, are determined in the following manner:

$$c'_{2Q}=\frac{(n_{12}+1)^2-4(n_{12}-1)^2\cos^2 2k_2y}{(1+n_{12})\sqrt{(1-3n_{12})(n_{12}-3)}};\quad c'_{1Q}=\frac{(n_{21}+1)^2-4(n_{21}-1)^2\cos^2 2k_1u}{(n_{21}+1)\sqrt{(1-3n_{21})(n_{21}-3)}}. \qquad (205)$$

As we see from (203), (204) and (205), the differential velocities of $\bar{V}$, $\bar{T}$ and $\bar{Q}$ waves have real values only in that case where the wave impedance ratio of the layered medium is found within the range $\frac{1}{3}\leqslant n_{12}\leqslant 3$, and for critical cases $n_{12}=\frac{1}{3}$ and $n_{12}=3$, the differential velocities of all modes in the first and second layers tend to infinity. However, for the points $u=0$ and $y=0$ in the layered medium, when $n_{12}\to 3$, the differential velocities approach zero, i.e., $c'_{2T}\to 0$ and $c'_{1V}\to 0$, and when $n_{12}\to\frac{1}{3}$, we then have $c'_{1T}\to 0$ and $c'_{2V}\to 0$. In those waves, for intensity waves at points $u=0$ and $y=0$, we always have $c'_{1Q}\to 0$ and $c'_{2Q}\to 0$.

When the wave impedance ratio is larger than three or smaller than one third, the formulas for the differential velocities, (203), (204) and (205), break down.

For the illustration in Fig. 21, graphs based on (203), (204) and (205) give the distribution of velocities and of attenuation constants in an infinite periodically layered medium, assuming $\frac{W_1}{W_2}=\frac{2}{1}$; $c_1=$ $=c_2$. From Fig. 21, we see clearly that if there is a mismatch of wave impedances $n_{12}=\frac{W_1}{W_2}=2$, then the distribution of differential velocities and of attenuation constants for different modes becomes highly complicated. This attests to the complicated shape of the phase travel-time curve and the uneven distribution of the amplitudes of the sinusoidal oscillations at points in the medium. For

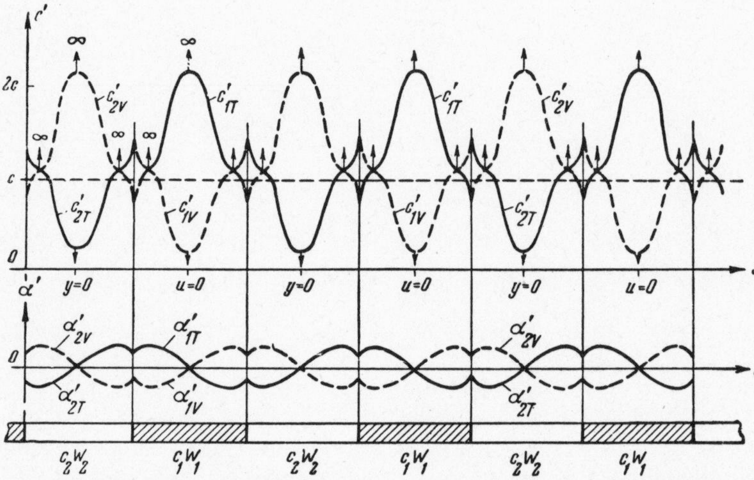

Fig. 21. Distribution of differential velocities of propagation c' and of attenuation constants α' of $\overline{V}$ and $\overline{T}$ waves in a periodically layered medium, when $\operatorname{tg} k_1l_1 = \operatorname{tg} k_2l_2 = \sqrt{3}$; $n_{12}=\frac{W_1}{W_2}=2$ (the case of transparency or complete transmission on the part of the periodically layered medium). For simplicity, we assume $c_1 = c_2 = c$. Arrows show the direction of motion of points, when the wave impedance ratio tends to the critical value $n_{12} \to 3$.

the case where the wave impedance ratio tends to the critical value $n_{12} \to 3$, Fig. 21 shows, by arrowheads, the direction of motion of the corresponding points on the graph (c'_{2V} and c'_{1T} tend to infinity, while c'_{1V} and c'_{2T} tend to zero, for points $u=0$ and $y=0$).

Up to this point in the present section, we have been considering the microstructure of waves traversing a periodically layered medium. Let us now proceed to a treatment of the integral wave characteristics of a layered medium which will characterize the external wave pattern existing in the medium.

The Integral Propagation Constants $\vec{S}_V$ and $\vec{S}_T$

The wave characteristics for the finite baseline $2l_1$ and $2l_2$ (cf. Fig. 16), i.e., the integral propagation constants for the entire first layer and the entire second layer, are determined, as usual, by means of integrating the differential propagation constants. With

$\vec{D}_1$ and $\vec{D}_2$ known from (187) and (188), for a periodically layered medium, we find, on the basis of (29) and (30), the integral propagation constants for the first layer:

$$\left.\begin{aligned}\vec{S}_{1V}=\int_{-l_1}^{+l_1}\vec{D}_{1V}du=\bar{q}_{01}\int_{-l_1}^{+l_1}\frac{A_1-\operatorname{sh}2\bar{q}_{01}u}{B_1-\operatorname{ch}2\bar{q}_{01}u}du,\\ \vec{S}_{1T}=\int_{-l_1}^{+l_1}\vec{D}_{1T}du=\bar{q}_{01}\int_{-l_1}^{+l_1}\frac{B_1-\operatorname{ch}2\bar{q}_{01}u}{A_1-\operatorname{sh}2\bar{q}_{01}u}du,\end{aligned}\right\} \tag{206}$$

and for the second layer:

$$\left.\begin{aligned}\vec{S}_{2V}=\int_{-l_2}^{+l_2}\vec{D}_{2V}dy=\bar{q}_{02}\int_{-l_2}^{+l_2}\frac{A_2-\operatorname{sh}2\bar{q}_{02}y}{B_2-\operatorname{ch}2\bar{q}_{02}y}dy,\\ \vec{S}_{2T}=\int_{-l_2}^{+l_2}\vec{D}_{2T}dy=\bar{q}_{02}\int_{-l_2}^{+l_2}\frac{B_2-\operatorname{ch}2\bar{q}_{02}y}{A_2-\operatorname{sh}2\bar{q}_{02}y}dy,\end{aligned}\right\} \tag{207}$$

where the quantities A_1; A_2; B_1 and B_2 are dependent on the integration variables u and y, and are related by (184) and (186).

We first determine the integral propagation constant of a velocity wave for the second layer, i.e., $\vec{S}_{2V}$, for which we rewrite the expression, replacing the hyperbolic functions by exponential functions:

$$\vec{S}_{2V}=\frac{1}{2}\int_{-l_2}^{+l_2}\frac{2A_2-(e^{2\bar{q}_{02}y}-e^{-2\bar{q}_{02}y})}{2B_2-(e^{2\bar{q}_{02}y}+e^{-2\bar{q}_{02}y})}d(2\bar{q}_{02}y). \tag{208}$$

The solution of that integral is found by means of substitution:

$$e^{2\bar{q}_{02}y}=z;\ e^{-2\bar{q}_{02}y}=\frac{1}{z};\ d(2\bar{q}_{02}y)=\frac{dz}{z}. \tag{209}$$

The integral in (208), with the new definitions taken into account, appears as:

$$\vec{S}_{2V}=\frac{1}{2}\int_{z_1}^{z_2}\frac{\left(2A_2-z+\frac{1}{z}\right)dz}{\left(2B_2-z-\frac{1}{z}\right)z}=\frac{1}{2}\int_{z_1}^{z_2}\frac{z^2-2A_2z-1}{z^2-2B_2z+1}dz, \tag{210}$$

where the new limits of integration $z_1=e^{-2\bar{q}_{02}l_2}$; $z_2=e^{2\bar{q}_{02}l_2}$. We next present the integrand, according to an expansion of rational functions, as follows:

$$\vec{S}_{2V}=\frac{1}{2}\int_{z_1}^{z_2}\left[\frac{2z-2(A_2+B_2)}{z^2-2B_2z+1}-\frac{1}{z}\right]dz, \tag{211}$$

or in the form of a series of integrals:

$$\vec{S}_{2V}=\int_{z_1}^{z_2}\frac{zdz}{z^2-2B_2z+1}-(A_2+B_2)\int_{z_1}^{z_2}\frac{dz}{z^2-2B_2z+1}-$$

$$-\frac{1}{2}\int_{z_1}^{z_2}\frac{dz}{z}=I_1-(A_2+B_2)I_2-\frac{1}{2}I_3. \tag{212}$$

Making use of a table of integrals, we may determine values: I_1; I_2; I_3:

$$\left.\begin{aligned}I_1&=\frac{1}{2}\ln(z^2-2B_2z+1)+\frac{B_2}{2A_2}\ln\left(\frac{z-B_2-A_2}{z-B_2+A_2}\right);\\I_2&=\frac{1}{2A_2}\ln\left(\frac{z-B_2-A_2}{z-B_2+A_2}\right);\\I_3&=\ln z,\end{aligned}\right\} \tag{213}$$

where we employ equation $A_2=\sqrt{B_2^2-1}$ [cf. (184)]. Substituting the values of the integrals in (213) into (212), we get:

$$\vec{S}_{2V}=\frac{1}{2}\ln\left[\left(z^2-2B_2\cdot z+1\right)\cdot\frac{1}{z}\right]\Bigg|_{z_1}^{z_2}-\frac{1}{2}\ln\left(\frac{z-B_2-A_2}{z-B_2+A_2}\right|_{z_1}^{z_2}, \tag{214}$$

or, after substitution of the limits of integration:

$$\vec{S}_{2V}=\frac{1}{2}\ln\left(\frac{e^{2\bar{q}_{02}l_2}-2B_2+e^{-2\bar{q}_{02}l_2}}{e^{2\bar{q}_{02}l_2}-2B_2+e^{-2\bar{q}_{02}l_2}}\right)-$$

$$-\frac{1}{2}\ln\left[\frac{\left(e^{2\bar{q}_{02}l_2}-B_2-A_2\right)\left(e^{-2\bar{q}_{02}l_2}-B_2+A_2\right)}{\left(e^{2\bar{q}_{02}l_2}-B_2+A_2\right)\left(e^{-2\bar{q}_{02}l_2}-B_2-A_2\right)}\right]. \tag{215}$$

Taking note of the fact that the first term vanishes, we transform the second term:

$$\vec{S}_{2V}=\frac{1}{2}\ln\left[\frac{(\operatorname{sh}2q_{02}l_2+\operatorname{ch}2\bar{q}_{02}l_2-B_2+A_2)(\operatorname{ch}2\bar{q}_{02}l_2-\operatorname{sh}2\bar{q}_{02}l_2-B_2-A_2)}{(\operatorname{sh}2\bar{q}_{02}l_2+\operatorname{ch}2\bar{q}_{02}l_2-B_2+A_2)(\operatorname{ch}2\bar{q}_{02}l_2-\operatorname{sh}2\bar{q}_{02}l_2-B_2+A_2)}\right], \tag{216}$$

or, multiplying through the expressions within parentheses, we obtain:

$$\vec{S}_{2V}=\frac{1}{2}\ln\left[\frac{1+\dfrac{A_2\operatorname{sh}2\bar{q}_{02}l_2}{B_2\operatorname{ch}2\bar{q}_{02}l_2-1}}{1-\dfrac{A_2\operatorname{sh}2\bar{q}_{02}l_2}{B_2\operatorname{ch}2\bar{q}_{02}l_2-1}}\right]. \tag{217}$$

After rather cumbersome operations, we eventually obtain the following value for the integral propagation constant in the second layer, for a velocity wave:

$$\vec{S}_{2V}=\ln\left(\frac{1+R_{2V}}{1-R_{2V}}\right)=2\operatorname{arcth}R_{2V}, \tag{218}$$

where we define:

$$R_{2V}=\operatorname{th}\bar{q}_{02}l_2\sqrt{\frac{(\overline{W}_1\operatorname{th}\bar{q}_{01}l_1+\overline{W}_2\operatorname{th}\bar{q}_{02}l_2)(\overline{W}_1+\overline{W}_2\operatorname{th}\bar{q}_{01}l_1\cdot\operatorname{th}\bar{q}_{02}l_2)}{(\overline{W}_1\operatorname{th}\bar{q}_{02}l_2+\overline{W}_2\operatorname{th}\bar{q}_{01}l_1)(\overline{W}_2+\overline{W}_1\operatorname{th}\bar{q}_{01}l_1\cdot\operatorname{th}q_{02}l_2)}}. \tag{219}$$

The integral propagation constant for a velocity wave in the first medium may be obtained by similar integration of the differential propagation constants $\vec{D}_{1V}$. However, by making use of the symmetry of the problem with respect to the first and second layers, we may state the result by means of interchange of subscripts *1* and *2*:

$$\vec{S}_{1V}=\ln\left(\frac{1+R_{1V}}{1-R_1}\right)=2\operatorname{Arth}R_{1V}, \tag{220}$$

where we have defined:

$$R_{1V}=\operatorname{th}\bar{q}_{01}l_1\sqrt{\frac{(\overline{W}_1\operatorname{th}\bar{q}_{01}l_1+\overline{W}_2\operatorname{th}\bar{q}_{02}l_2)(\overline{W}_2+\overline{W}_1\operatorname{th}\bar{q}_{01}l_1\cdot\operatorname{th}\bar{q}_{02}l_2)}{(\overline{W}_1\operatorname{th}\bar{q}_{02}l_2+\overline{W}_2\operatorname{th}\bar{q}_{01}l_1)(\overline{W}_1+\overline{W}_2\operatorname{th}\bar{q}_{01}l_1\cdot\operatorname{th}\bar{q}_{02}l_2)}}. \tag{221}$$

Having integral propagation constants for the velocity wave separately for the first (220) and the second (218) layer, we may now obtain, by summation, the integral propagation constant over the baseline $2l_1+2l_2$, i.e., for the two layers[1]:

$$\vec{S}_{\text{II}V}=\vec{S}_{1V}+\vec{S}_{2V}=\ln\left(\frac{1+R_{\text{II}}}{1-R_{\text{II}}}\right)=2\operatorname{Arth}R_{\text{II}}, \tag{222}$$

where we have defined:

[1] The same value of the integral propagation constant for a velocity wave over the baseline $2l_1+2l_2$ may be obtained by using the accepted four-pole network techniques.

$$R_{\text{II}} = \sqrt{\frac{(\overline{W}_1 \operatorname{th} \bar{q}_{01} l_1 + \overline{W}_2 \operatorname{th} \bar{q}_{02} l_2)(\overline{W}_1 \operatorname{th} \bar{q}_{02} l_2 + \overline{W}_2 \operatorname{th} \bar{q}_{01} l_1)}{(\overline{W}_1 + \overline{W}_2 \operatorname{th} q_{01} l_1 \cdot \operatorname{th} \bar{q}_{02} l_2)(\overline{W}_2 + \overline{W}_1 \operatorname{th} \bar{q}_{01} l_1 \cdot \operatorname{th} \bar{q}_{02} l_2)}}. \quad (223)$$

The integral propagation constant $\vec{S}_{\text{II}V}$, after transformations, takes on the following definitive form[1]:

$$\vec{S}_{\text{II}V} = \operatorname{Arch}\left[\frac{(\overline{W}_1 + \overline{W}_2)^2}{4\overline{W}_1 W_2} \cdot \operatorname{ch} 2(\bar{q}_{01} l_1 + \bar{q}_{02} l_2) - \frac{(\overline{W}_1 - \overline{W}_2)^2}{4\overline{W}_1 \overline{W}_2} \operatorname{ch} 2(\bar{q}_{01} l_1 - \bar{q}_{02} l_2)\right] \quad (224)$$

or

$$\vec{S}_{\text{II}V} = 2 \operatorname{Arsh} \sqrt{\frac{(\overline{W}_1 + \overline{W}_2)^2}{4\overline{W}_1 \overline{W}_2} \operatorname{sh}^2(\bar{q}_{01} l_1 + \bar{q}_{02} l_2) - \frac{(\overline{W}_1 - \overline{W}_2)^2}{4\overline{W}_1 \overline{W}_2} \operatorname{sh}^2(\bar{q}_{01} l_1 - \bar{q}_{02} l_2)}. \quad (225)$$

We may now proceed to a determination of the integral propagation constants for pressure waves in the first and second layers. It remains for us to evaluate the integral in (207). For this purpose, we shall, as in previous examples, replace the hyperbolic functions by exponential functions:

$$\vec{S}_{2T} = \frac{1}{2} \int_{-l_2}^{+l_2} \frac{2B_2 - (e^{2\bar{q}_{02} y} + e^{-2\bar{q}_{02} y})}{2A_2 - (e^{2\bar{q}_{02} y} - e^{-2\bar{q}_{02} y})} \, d(2\bar{q}_{02} y). \quad (226)$$

We then use the substitution $z = e^{2\bar{q}_{02} y}$; whereupon the integral becomes:

$$\vec{S}_{2T} = \frac{1}{2} \int_{z_1}^{z_2} \frac{\left(2B_2 - z - \frac{1}{z}\right) dz}{\left(2A_2 - z + \frac{1}{z}\right) z} = \frac{1}{2} \int_{z_1}^{z_2} \frac{(z^2 - 2B_2 z + 1)\, dz}{(z^2 - 2A_2 z - 1)\, z}, \quad (227)$$

where the new limits of integration are: $z_1 = e^{-2\bar{q}_{02} l_2}$; $z_2 = e^{2\bar{q}_{02} l_2}$. We present the integrand in the following form:

$$\vec{S}_{2T} = \frac{1}{2} \int_{z_1}^{z_2} \left[\frac{2z - 2(A_2 + B_2)}{z^2 - 2A_2 z - 1} - \frac{1}{z}\right] dz. \quad (228)$$

[1] It may be shown, in the case $p = i\omega$, that the propagation constant $\vec{S}_{\text{II}V}$ does not change in value when the baseline $2l_1 + 2l_2$ for which $\vec{S}_{\text{II}V}$ was determined is arbitrarily shifted relative to the interfaces of the layered medium. This comes about, in any case, owing to the fact that the values of the differential propagation constants (190) for the adjacent identical layers are symmetric about the middle of each layer.

Making use of a table of integrals (213), we arrive at the following value for the integral propagation constant of a pressure wave in the second layer:

$$\vec{S}_{2T}=\frac{1}{2}\ln\left\{\frac{(e^{2\bar{q}_{02}l_2}-2A_2-e^{-2\bar{q}_{02}l_2})\left[e^{2\bar{q}_{02}l_2}-(A_2-B_2)\right]\left[e^{-2\bar{q}_{02}l_2}-(A_2+B_2)\right]}{(e^{-2\bar{q}_{02}l_2}-2A_2-e^{2\bar{q}_{02}l_2})\left[e^{2\bar{q}_{02}l_2}-(A_2+B_2)\right]\left[e^{-2\bar{q}_{02}l_2}-(A_2-A_2)\right]}\right\} \quad (229)$$

or finally, after several transformations, substituting the values of A_2 and B_2 [see the definitions given in (184)], we obtain:

$$\vec{S}_{2T}=\ln\left(\frac{1+R_{2T}}{1-R_{2T}}\right)=2\,\mathrm{Arth}\,R_{1T}, \quad (230)$$

where we define:

$$R_{2T}=\mathrm{th}\,\bar{q}_{02}l_2\sqrt{\frac{(\overline{W}_1\,\mathrm{th}\,\bar{q}_{02}l_2+\overline{W}_2\,\mathrm{th}\,\bar{q}_{01}l_1)(\overline{W}_2+\overline{W}_1\,\mathrm{th}\,\bar{q}_{01}l_1\,\mathrm{th}\,\bar{q}_{02}l_2)}{(\overline{W}_1\,\mathrm{th}\,\bar{q}_{01}l_1+\overline{W}_2\,\mathrm{th}\,\bar{q}_{02}l_2)(\overline{W}_1+\overline{W}_2\,\mathrm{th}\,\bar{q}_{01}l_1\,\mathrm{th}\,\bar{q}_{02}l_2)}}\,. \quad (231)$$

The integral propagation constant of a pressure wave in the first layer over a baseline $2l_1$ may be written, taking in view the symmetry of the problem, by means of interchanging subscripts *1* and *2*:

$$\vec{S}_{1T}=\ln\left(\frac{1+R_{1T}}{1-R_{1T}}\right)=2\,\mathrm{Arth}\,R_{1T}, \quad (232)$$

where we define:

$$R_{1T}=\mathrm{th}\,\bar{q}_{01}l_1\sqrt{\frac{(\overline{W}_1\,\mathrm{th}\,\bar{q}_{02}l_2+\overline{W}_2\,\mathrm{th}\,\bar{q}_{01}l_1)(\overline{W}_1+\overline{W}_2\,\mathrm{th}\,\bar{q}_{01}l_1\,\mathrm{th}\,\bar{q}_{02}l_2)}{(\overline{W}_1\,\mathrm{th}\,q_{01}l_1+\overline{W}_2\,\mathrm{th}\,\bar{q}_{02}l_2)(\overline{W}_2+\overline{W}_1\,\mathrm{th}\,\bar{q}_{01}l_1\,\mathrm{th}\,\bar{q}_{02}l_2)}}\,. \quad (233)$$

Having obtained the integral propagation constants of a pressure wave for the first (232) and second (230) layers, we then determine the integral propagation constant for two layers over a baseline $2l_1+2l_2$ (cf. Fig. 16):

$$\vec{S}_{\mathrm{II}T}=\vec{S}_{1T}+\vec{S}_{2T}=\ln\left[\frac{(1+R_{1T})(1+R_{2T})}{(1-R_{1T})(1-R_{2T})}\right] \quad (234)$$

or, after transformations, we end up with:

$$\vec{S}_{\mathrm{II}T}=\ln\left(\frac{1+R_{\mathrm{II}}}{1-R_{\mathrm{II}}}\right)=2\,\mathrm{Arth}\,R_{\mathrm{II}}, \quad (235)$$

where R_{II} is given by (223), and the propagation constants for velocity and pressure waves over a baseline $2l_1+2l_2$ are consequently equal, $\vec{S}_{\mathrm{II}V}=\vec{S}_{\mathrm{II}T}$. In addition, determining the integral propagation constant for an intensity wave over a baseline $2l_1 + 2l_2$, we obtain $\vec{S}_{\Pi Q} = \frac{1}{2}(\vec{S}_{\Pi V} + \vec{S}_{\Pi T}) = \vec{S}_{\Pi V}$ and, consequently, we end up with:

$$\vec{S}_{\Pi V} = \vec{S}_{\Pi T} = \vec{S}_{\Pi Q}. \quad (236)$$

Terming an interval of a periodically layered medium of length $2l_1 + 2l_2$ as in Fig. 16 a section, we shall have, for n sections through a layered medium, the following integral propagation constant:

$$\vec{S}_{\Pi V} = \vec{S}_{\Pi T} = n \ln \left(\frac{1 + R_{\Pi}}{1 - R_{\Pi}} \right) = 2n \operatorname{Arth} R_{\Pi}. \quad (237)$$

Integral Wave Properties Over Baselines $2l_1$ and $2l_2$

Let us now rewrite the values obtained for the integral propagation constants of the first and second layers for the case of the steady-state mode of oscillations ($p = i\omega$), assuming that resistive losses are absent in the layers. For a velocity wave, we have:

$$\left.\begin{aligned} \vec{S}_{1V} &= i2 \operatorname{arctg} \left[\operatorname{tg} \omega\tau_1 \sqrt{\frac{(W_1 \operatorname{tg} \omega\tau_1 + W_2 \operatorname{tg} \omega\tau_2)(W_2 - W_1 \operatorname{tg} \omega\tau_1 \operatorname{tg} \omega\tau_2)}{(W_1 \operatorname{tg} \omega\tau_2 + W_2 \operatorname{tg} \omega\tau_1)(W_1 - W_2 \operatorname{tg} \omega\tau_1 \operatorname{tg} \omega\tau_2)}} \right], \\ \vec{S}_{2V} &= i2 \operatorname{arctg} \left[\operatorname{tg} \omega\tau_2 \sqrt{\frac{(W_1 \operatorname{tg} \omega\tau_1 + W_2 \operatorname{tg} \omega\tau_2)(W_1 - W_2 \operatorname{tg} \omega\tau_1 \cdot \operatorname{tg} \omega\tau_2)}{(W_1 \operatorname{tg} \omega\tau_2 + W_2 \operatorname{tg} \omega\tau_1)(W_2 - W_1 \operatorname{tg} \omega\tau_1 \cdot \operatorname{tg} \omega\tau_2)}} \right], \end{aligned}\right\} \quad (238)$$

and for a pressure wave:

$$\left.\begin{aligned} \vec{S}_{1T} &= i2 \operatorname{arctg} \left[\operatorname{tg} \omega\tau_1 \sqrt{\frac{(W_1 \operatorname{tg} \omega\tau_2 + W_2 \operatorname{tg} \omega\tau_1)(W_1 - W_2 \operatorname{tg} \omega\tau_1 \cdot \operatorname{tg} \omega\tau_2)}{(W_1 \operatorname{tg} \omega\tau_1 + W_2 \operatorname{tg} \omega\tau_2)(W_2 - W_1 \operatorname{tg} \omega\tau_1 \cdot \operatorname{tg} \omega\tau_2)}} \right]; \\ \vec{S}_{2T} &= i2 \operatorname{arctg} \left[\operatorname{tg} \omega\tau_2 \sqrt{\frac{(W_1 \cdot \operatorname{tg} \omega\tau_2 + W_2 \operatorname{tg} \omega\tau_1)(W_2 - W_1 \cdot \operatorname{tg} \omega\tau_1 \cdot \operatorname{tg} \omega\tau_2)}{(W_1 \operatorname{tg} \omega\tau_1 + W_2 \operatorname{tg} \omega\tau_2)(W_1 - W_2 \operatorname{tg} \omega\tau_1 \cdot \operatorname{tg} \omega\tau_2)}} \right], \end{aligned}\right\} \quad (239)$$

where: $\tau_1 = \frac{l_1}{c_1}$ is the half time of travel of a homogeneous wave through the first layer; $\tau_1 = \frac{l_2}{c_2}$ is the same for the second layer, and ω is the frequency of the oscillations.

It is of interest to note the general property of the integral propagation constants so obtained (238, 239), for the case of steady-state sinusoidal oscillations: when the radicands are greater than zero, then $\vec{S}_1$ and $\vec{S}_2$ have no real parts and, accordingly, the attenuation constants of the different modes in the layers $\alpha_s = 0$. On the other hand, in the case where the radicands are less than zero, attenuation of all modes occurs in the layers of the medium $\alpha_s \neq 0$.

The phase-shift constants β_s occur by multiples πn, where $n=1$, 2, 3, according to the number of waves accommodated per layer. The multiplicity of the integral phase constant $\beta_s = \pi n$, where $n = 2, 4, 6$, points to the fact that the motions of the interfaces of each layer are in phase, while in the case $\beta_s = \pi \cdot n$, where $n = 1, 3, 5$, the motions of the interfaces of each layer are 180° out of phase.

Let us point out one more important property of $\vec{S}_1$ and $\vec{S}_2$, with the assumption that $n_{12} = \frac{W_1}{W_2}$, and that τ_1 and τ_2 are finite constant magnitudes. It may be shown that when the frequency is ranged upward from 0 to ∞, the state of transparency of the layers ($\alpha_s = 0$) is replaced by the state of attenuation of different modes of waves traversing the layers (and conversely) simultaneously for the first and second layers. Actually, when the frequency $\omega \to 0$, the radicands are positive, provided the conditions indicated are satisfied. Assuming that the frequency ω varies from 0 to ∞, we then consider the change in sign of the radicand brought about by the sign-alternating tangent function. The radicands of all of the integral propagation constants in (238) and (239) are dependent on four identical expressions in parentheses, which may be combined differently. Therefore, when at some frequency ω_c one or an odd number of values found between parentheses change in sign, this has a simultaneous effect on all of the other radicands and consequently $\vec{S}_1$ and $\vec{S}_2$ at frequency ω_c determine the simultaneous transition of the layers of the medium from one state to another. In other words, there can be no such phenomenon taking place in a periodically layered medium at any fixed frequency, where one layer is transparent or reflectionless ($\alpha_s = 0$), and the other suffers attenuation. Frequencies ω_c, at which a transition from one state to another occurs in the layered medium, will be known in the subsequent discussion as cut-off frequencies.

Consider several particular cases of integral propagation constants for the first and second layers (238) and (239):

1. Suppose that $\omega \to 0$, then the integral propagation constant of a velocity wave for the first layer may, according to the generally familiar relation $\operatorname{tg} x \simeq x$, where x is sufficiently small in value, be rewritten as follows:

$$\vec{S}_{1v} = i2\omega_1\tau_1 \sqrt{\frac{(W_1\tau_1 + W_2\tau_2)(W_2 - W_1\omega^2\tau_1\tau_2)}{(W_1\tau_2 + W_2\tau_1)(W_1 - W_2\omega^2\tau_1\tau_2)}} = 0 + i\beta_{1v}. \tag{240}$$

Discarding terms of the second order of smallness (ω^2) and using (75) to determine the integral velocity of propagation, we arrive at:

$$c_{1V}=c_1\sqrt{\frac{W_1(W_1\tau_2+W_2\tau_1)}{W_2(W_1\tau_1+W_2\tau_2)}}. \tag{241}$$

Comparing the value of c_{1V} with that of the differential velocity c'_{1V} (194), obtained under the same constraint $\omega\to 0$, we find that the two are equal $c_{1V}=c'_{1V}$. It may similarly be shown that:

$$c_{2V}=c'_{2V};\ c_{1T}=c'_{1T};\ c_{2T}=c'_{2T}. \tag{242}$$

2. Suppose $\operatorname{tg}\omega\tau_2\to\infty$, which case corresponds to $2l_2=\frac{\lambda_2}{2}$.

The integral propagation constants take on the following values:

$$\left.\begin{aligned}\vec{S}_{2V}&=\vec{S}_{2T}=i2\operatorname{arctg}\infty=0+i\pi,\\ \vec{S}_{1V}&=\vec{S}_{1T}=i2\operatorname{arctg}[\operatorname{tg}\omega\tau_1]=0+i\frac{2\omega l_1}{c_1},\end{aligned}\right\} \tag{243}$$

i.e., in that case, the integral velocities in the first and second layers correspond to the computed velocities $c_2=c_{2V}=c_{2T}$ and $c_1=c_{1V}=c_{1T}$. The integral attenuation constants vanish, which corresponds to a reflectionless periodically layered medium.

3. Consider the most general case $\operatorname{tg}\omega\tau_1=\operatorname{tg}\omega\tau_2=\operatorname{tg}\omega\tau$, where $\operatorname{tg}\omega\tau$ varies over the range $0<\operatorname{tg}\omega\tau<\infty$ (we assume $c_1=c_2=c;\ l_2=l_1=l$). Then the integral propagation constants assume the values:

$$\left.\begin{aligned}\vec{S}_{2V}&=\vec{S}_{1T}=i2\operatorname{arctg}\sqrt{\frac{n_{12}-\operatorname{tg}^2\omega\tau}{\operatorname{ctg}^2\omega\tau-n_{12}}},\\ \vec{S}_{1V}&=\vec{S}_{2T}=i2\operatorname{arctg}\sqrt{\frac{1-n_{12}\operatorname{tg}^2\omega\tau}{n_{12}\operatorname{ctg}^2\omega\tau-1}},\end{aligned}\right\} \tag{244}$$

where we have $n_{12}=\frac{W_1}{W_2}$. In addition, we determine the integral constants of an intensity wave for the first and second layers, using (244):

$$\vec{S}_{1Q}=\frac{1}{2}(\vec{S}_{1V}+\vec{S}_{1T})=\vec{S}_{2Q}=\frac{1}{2}(\vec{S}_{2V}+\vec{S}_{2T})=$$
$$=i\operatorname{arctg}\left[\frac{1+n_{12}\operatorname{tg}\omega\tau}{\sqrt{(n_{12}-\operatorname{tg}^2\omega\tau)(1-n_{12}\operatorname{tg}^2\omega\tau)}}\right]. \tag{245}$$

The cut-off frequencies at which the transition of the integral propagation constants (244) and (245) from imaginary to real values (more accurately, complex values) takes place and vice versa is determined, as may be readily seen, by the equations

$$n_{12} = \mathrm{tg}^2\, \omega_{c_1}\tau, \tag{246a}$$

$$n_{12} = \mathrm{tg}^2\, \omega_{c_2}\tau. \tag{246b}$$

Figure 22 gives the regions of transparency (regions of imaginary values of the integral propagation constants) represented as

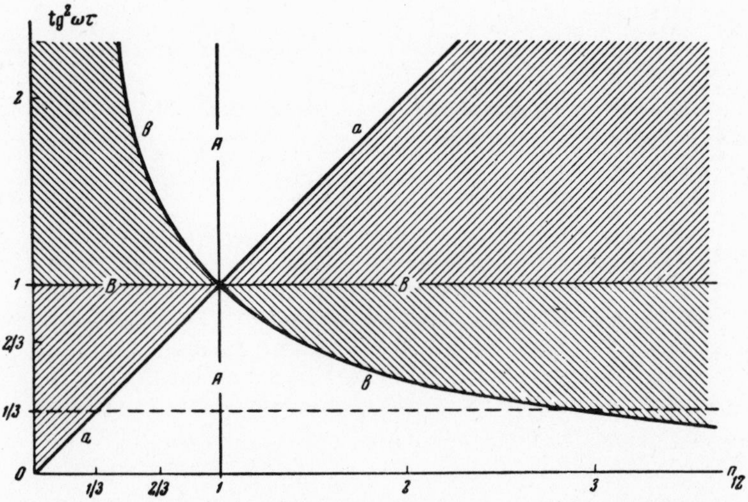

Fig. 22. Regions of imaginary (A) and complex (B) values of the integral propagation constants of the first and second layers for the particular case $\mathrm{tg}\,\omega\tau_1 = \mathrm{tg}\,\omega\tau_2 = \mathrm{tg}\,\omega\tau$, which corresponds to regions of transparency (A) and of attenuation (B) of the waves traversing a periodically layered medium.

the clear areas, and the regions of attenuation of the wave traversing the layers (regions of complex values of $\vec{S}$) as the hatched areas. The constraints (246) are represented on that plane by the lines a and $в$.

Figure 23 presents a graph of the integral propagation constants for a baseline equal to the thickness of the layer, as a function of the wave impedance ratio $n_{12} = \frac{W_1}{W_2}$, for the particular value of the tangent $\mathrm{tg}\,\omega\tau = \frac{1}{\sqrt{3}}$, i.e., when confined to the layers of the periodically layered medium $2l = \frac{\lambda}{6}$, where $\lambda = \frac{2\pi c}{\omega}$. The transparency band is represented on the graph by the interval a — $в$.

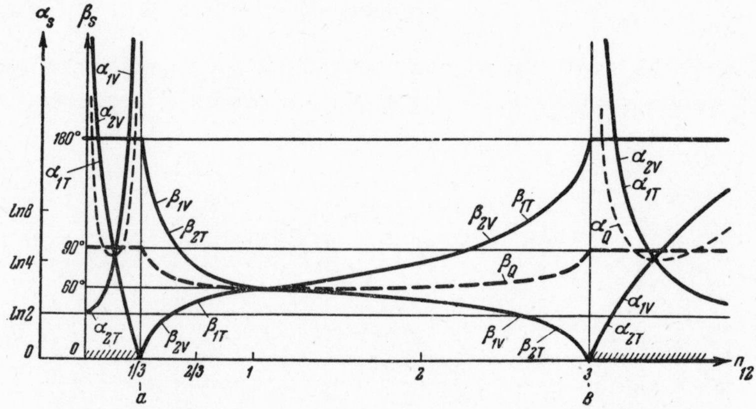

Fig. 23. Variation in the integral propagation constants of the first and second layers of a periodically layered medium, as a function of the ratio $n_{12} = \frac{W_1}{W_2}$, for the particular case $\operatorname{tg} \omega\tau_1 = \operatorname{tg} \omega\tau_2 = \frac{1}{\sqrt{3}}$. The band $a - в$ (cf. Fig. 22) is characterized by the complete absence of attenuation of the waves in layers 1 and 2, and consequently also in the periodically layered medium as a whole.

Let us investigate the observed variation of the form of the graph plotted for $\vec{S}$ (Fig. 23) with the variation in the value of $\operatorname{tg}^2 \omega\tau$, other conditions remaining unchanged. This corresponds to a treatment of the functions $\vec{S} = f(n_{12}, \operatorname{tg}^2 \omega\tau)$ [cf. (244)], as a function of the variation of $\operatorname{tg}^2 \omega\tau$. As $\operatorname{tg}^2 \omega\tau$ is varied from zero to unity, the transparency band a — $в$ displayed in Fig. 23 contracts, and at the value $\operatorname{tg}^2 \omega\tau = 1$, the band degenerates into a point at $n_{12} = 1$ (cf. also Fig. 22).

With a further increase in the value of $\operatorname{tg}^2 \omega\tau$ from 1 to ∞, the transparency band $в$ — a in Fig. 22 begins to expand, although in that case the graph of the integral propagation constant $\vec{S}$ has an inverse form, compared to the graph of $\vec{S}$ in Fig. 23, signifying the following: by inverting the graph in Fig. 23 about the axis $n_{12} = 1$ through 180°, we obtain a graph of $\vec{S}$ similar to the one derived for values of $\operatorname{tg}^2 \omega\tau$ ranging from 1 to ∞. It follows hence that the wave properties of layers in the layered medium, in the case of the transition through the cut-off point $tg^2\,\omega\tau = 1$, reverse sharply to their opposites (the assumption still holds that resistive losses are absent). This means that as the function undergoes a transition through the value $tg^2\,\omega\tau = 1$, the first layer acquires the wave properties of the second layer, and conversely.

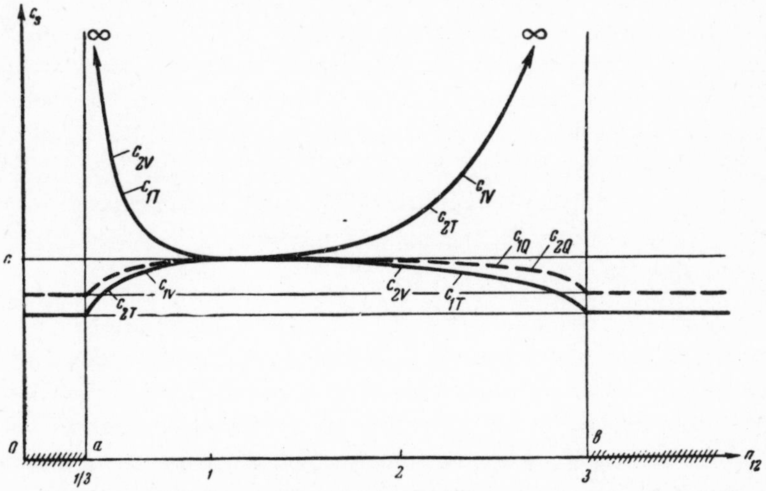

Fig. 24. Variation in the integral velocities of propagation of the first and second layers of a periodically layered medium as a function of the ratio $n_{12} = \frac{W_1}{W_2}$ for the particular case $tg\,\omega\tau_1 = tg\,\omega\tau_2 = \frac{1}{\sqrt{3}}$. For simplicity, we set $c_1 = c_2 = c$.

For the particular case in point, $\tau_1 = \tau_2 = \tau$, we determine the values of the integral velocities by substituting the values found for β_S (244) into the already familiar equation $c = \frac{\omega 2l}{\beta_S}$:

$$\left.\begin{aligned} c_{2V} = c_{1T} &= \frac{\omega l}{\operatorname{arctg}\sqrt{\dfrac{n_{12} - tg^2\,\omega\tau}{ctg^2\,\omega\tau - n_{12}}}}; \\ c_{1V} = c_{2T} &= \frac{\omega l}{\operatorname{arctg}\sqrt{\dfrac{1 - n_{12}\,tg^2\,\omega\tau}{n_{12}\,ctg^2\,\omega\tau - 1}}}; \\ c_{1Q} = c_{2Q} &= \frac{\omega 2l}{\operatorname{arctg}\left[\dfrac{(1 + n_{12}) \cdot tg\,\omega\tau}{\sqrt{(n_{12} - tg^2\,\omega\tau)(1 - n_{12}\,tg^2\,\omega\tau)}}\right]}. \end{aligned}\right\} \quad (247)$$

According to the formulas so obtained (247), a graph is plotted in Fig. 24 for the integral velocities $c = f(n_{12})$ of the first and second layers, as well as for different modes $\bar{V}$, $\bar{T}$ and $\bar{Q}$, with the assumption that $\operatorname{tg}\omega\tau = \frac{1}{\sqrt{3}}$.

We see from the graphs in Fig. 23, 24 that as the wave impedance ratio of the layers, n_{12}, ranges from 1 to 0 (i.e., when the wave impedance declines relatively in the first layer, and rises relatively in the second layer), the velocity of a $\bar{V}$ wave in the first layer is diminished, while it is stepped up in the second layer. When the cut-off point a (cf. Fig. 23 and Fig. 24) is reached, the $\bar{V}$ wave attains a state in which the extreme points of the first layer begin to move opposed in phase, while all points of the second layer are moving in phase (monolithically), which corresponds to the value of the velocity in the second medium $c_{2v} = \infty$ (in this connection, see Fig. 21).

For the $\bar{T}$ pressure waves, in the case of decrease in n_{12} from 1 to 0, we have the reverse picture: the integral velocity in the first layer, c_{1T}, increases, while it decreases in the second layer, with a state arising at the cut-off point a where the extreme points of the second layer, phase-shifted through 180°, experience mechanical pressures, and the entire first layer experiences pressures moving in phase, i.e., $c_{1T} = \infty$.

If we consider the variation of n_{12} from 1 to ∞, the properties of velocity and pressure waves in the first and second layer will exchange places (in accord with the symmetry of the problem with respect to the first and second layers, since $\operatorname{tg}\omega\tau_1 = \operatorname{tg}\omega\tau_2 = \operatorname{tg}\omega\tau$).

With respect to the intensity wave, it is worthy of note that, in the case under consideration $\operatorname{tg}\omega\tau < 1$ $\left(\operatorname{tg}\omega\tau = \frac{1}{\sqrt{3}}\right)$, as n_{12} varies from 1 to 0 and from 1 to ∞ (cf. Fig. 24), the integral velocity of that wave in the first and second layers decreases, however, without reaching the extreme zero or infinite values.

The Integral Wave Properties Over a Baseline $2l_1 + 2l_2$

Consider, finally, the integral wave properties of an infinite periodically layered medium (Fig. 16) extending over a baseline $2l_1 + 2l_2$, for steady-state oscillations. For this purpose, we may write in our new notation the integral propagation constant in (222), which, as shown by (236), is valid for all of the modes, $\bar{V}$, $\bar{T}$ and $\bar{Q}$:

$$\vec{S}_{II} = i\,2\,\mathrm{arctg}\sqrt{\frac{(W_1\,\mathrm{tg}\,\omega\tau_1 + W_2\,\mathrm{tg}\,\omega\tau_2)\cdot(W\,\mathrm{tg}\,\omega\tau_2 + W_2\,\mathrm{tg}\,\omega\tau_1)}{(W_1 - W_2\,\mathrm{tg}\,\omega\tau_1\cdot\mathrm{tg}\,\omega\tau_2)\cdot(W_2 - W_1\,\mathrm{tg}\,\omega\tau_1\cdot\mathrm{tg}\,\omega\tau_2)}}. \quad (248)$$

The baseline $2l_1 + 2l_2$, over which $\vec{S}_{II}$, is determined may be arbitrarily shifted with respect to the interfaces of the layered medium.

The integral propagation constant $\vec{S}_{II}$, may be written, according to (225), in another form:

$$\vec{S}_{II} = i\,\arcsin\sqrt{\frac{(W_1+W_2)^2}{4W_1W_2}\cdot\sin^2\omega(\tau_1+\tau_2) - \frac{(W_1-W_2)^2}{4W_1W_2}\sin^2\omega(\tau_1-\tau_2)}. \quad (249)$$

The value of $\vec{S}_{II_n}$ for the n-th number of sections of a layered medium (Fig. 16) is determined by the simple summation of the values of $\vec{S}_{II}$ for each section [cf. (237)].

On the basis of the considerations adduced above relating to the states of the first and second layers, consider the conditions governing the transition of a layered medium as a whole from the transparent state to an opaque state. According to (248), those conditions are due to the value of the radicand being equal to zero or to infinity, which yields the following relations (transcendental equations for the cut-off frequencies):

$$\left.\begin{aligned} &W_1\,\mathrm{tg}\,\omega\tau_1 + W_2\,\mathrm{tg}\,\omega\tau_2 = 0; \quad W_1\,\mathrm{tg}\,\omega\tau_2 + W_2\,\mathrm{tg}\,\omega\tau_1 = 0;\\ &W_1 - W_2\,\mathrm{tg}\,\omega\tau_1\cdot\mathrm{tg}\,\omega\tau_2 = 0; \quad W_2 - W_1\,\mathrm{g}\,\omega\tau_1\cdot\mathrm{tg}\,\omega\tau_2 = 0.\end{aligned}\right\} \quad (250)$$

From the equations obtained for the cut-off frequencies, assuming $n_{12} = \mathrm{const}$, frequencies ω_c, which delimit the regions of transparency from the opaque regions of a periodically layered medium, are defined.

Taking as the starting point (249), for which the transition from the transparent state of a periodically layered medium to the opaque state is determined by the value of a root equal to unity or to zero, we obtain the following equations for the cut-off frequencies:

$$\left.\begin{aligned} &\frac{(W_1+W_2)^2}{4W_1W_2}\cdot\sin^2\omega(\tau_1+\tau_2) - \frac{(W_1-W_2)^2}{4W_1W_2}\cdot\sin^2\omega(\tau_1-\tau_2) = 0,\\ &\frac{(W_1+W_2)^2}{4W_1W_2}\cdot\sin^2\omega(\tau_1+\tau_2) - \frac{(W_1-W_2)^2}{4W_1W_2}\cdot\sin^2\omega(\tau_1-\tau_2) = 1,\end{aligned}\right\} \quad (251)$$

which, naturally, are identical to the conditions (250).

Finally, the transparent regions of a periodically layered medium are determined by the inequalities:

$$0 \leqslant \frac{(W_1 \operatorname{tg} \omega\tau_1 + W_2 \operatorname{tg} \omega\tau_2)(W_1 \operatorname{tg} \omega\tau_2 + W_2 \operatorname{tg} \omega\tau_1)}{(W_1 - W_2 \operatorname{tg} \omega\tau_1 \cdot \operatorname{tg} \omega\tau_2)(W_2 - W_1 \operatorname{tg} \omega\tau_1 \cdot \operatorname{tg} \omega\tau_2)} \leqslant \infty, \qquad (252a)$$

or (identical with the above):

$$0 \leqslant \frac{(W_1 + W_2)^2}{4W_1W_2} \sin^2 \omega(\tau_1 + \tau_2) - \frac{(W_1 - W_2)^2}{4W_1W_2} \sin^2 \omega(\tau_1 - \tau_2) \leqslant 1. \qquad (252b)$$

Consider several particular cases for the integral propagation constants $\vec{S}_{\text{II}}$.

1. Suppose that $\omega \to 0$. In that case, the trigonometric functions sin and tg may be replaced by their angles. Then, (248) yields:

$$\vec{S}_{\text{II}} = i\, 2\omega \sqrt{\frac{(W_1\tau_1 + W_2\tau_2)(W_1\tau_2 + W_2\tau_1)}{(W_1 - W_2\omega^2\tau_1\tau_2)(W_2 - W_1\omega^2\tau_1\tau_2)}}. \qquad (253)$$

Assuming $n_{12} = \frac{W_1}{W_2}$ to be some finite quantity, and neglecting second order terms $[\omega^2]$, we have:

$$\vec{S}_{\text{II}} = i\, 2\omega \sqrt{\frac{(W_1\tau_1 + W_2\tau_2)(W_1\tau_2 + W_2\tau_1)}{W_1W_2}} = 0 + i\beta_{\text{II}}. \qquad (254)$$

The integral propagation velocity[1] in a section of a layered medium is determined in the usual way, with the integral phase constant β_{II} known:

$$c_{\text{II}} = \frac{\omega(2l_1 + 2l_2)}{\beta_{\text{II}}} = \frac{(l_1 + l_2)\sqrt{W_1W_2}}{\sqrt{(W_1\tau_1 + W_2\tau_2)(W_1\tau_2 + W_2\tau_1)}}, \qquad (255)$$

[1] The requirement $\omega \to 0$ may be replaced by the constraint $l_1 \to 0 \cdot l_2 \to 0$, assuming $l_1/l_2 = r =$ const, for some arbitrary finite value of frequency ω. In that case we obtain a homogeneous (for which see [22]) medium, the velocity in which is determined, for all modes and for any frequency, from a similar formula:

$$c_{\text{II}} = \frac{(r+1)\sqrt{W_1 \cdot W_2}}{\sqrt{\left(\frac{W_1}{c_1} \cdot r + \frac{W_2}{c_2}\right)\left(\frac{W_1}{c_2} + \frac{W_2}{c_1} \cdot r\right)}};$$

where c_1, c_2, W_1 and W_2 are velocities and wave impedances of elemental layers.

where $\tau_1 = \frac{l_1}{c_1}$; $\tau_2 = \frac{l_2}{c_2}$. Formulas similar to (255) are obtained in references [25, 27], while a detailed investigation for seismic purposes is entered into in [27].

The integral velocity (255) for a section in a layered medium, when $\omega \to 0$, may be obtained through another approach, if we resort to the (true) velocities found for discrete layers in the medium under study (194) and to the formula for the mean velocities from geometric seismics; in that case, when the wave impedance parameters W_1 and W_2 are taken into account in the values found for the velocities in discrete layers, the formula for the mean velocities becomes valid.

We shall now investigate the microstructure of an elastic wave in a periodically layered medium, with the assumption that $\omega \to 0$; $\tau_1 = \tau_2 = \tau$ $(c_1 = c_2 = c$ and $l_1 = l_2 = l)$. In that case, the differential velocities in the layers (194) take on the following values:

$$\left.\begin{aligned} c'_{1V} &= c'_{2T} = c\sqrt{\frac{W_1}{W_2}};\\ c'_{2V} &= c'_{1T} = c\sqrt{\frac{W_2}{W_1}};\\ c'_{1Q} &= c'_{2Q} = c\,\frac{2\sqrt{W_1 \cdot W_2}}{W_1 + W_2};\end{aligned}\right\} \qquad (256)$$

and the integral velocities over the baseline $2l_1 + 2l_2$ (255) are:

$$c_{\text{II}} = c_V = c_T = c_Q = c\,\frac{2\sqrt{W_1 W_2}}{W_1 + W_2}. \qquad (257)$$

In Fig. 25, we see a construction of phase travel-time curves for $\bar{V}$, $\bar{T}$ and $\bar{Q}$ modes in a periodically layered medium, based on (256) and (257). The curves reflect the microstructure of the resultant wave traversing a layered medium, with the constraint $\omega \to 0$ observed, or when the wavelength is much larger than the length of a section $2l_1 + 2l_2$.

Curve A in Fig. 25 is constructed for the wave impedance ratio $n_{12} = 1$, curve B for the ratio $n_{12} = 5$, and curve C for the ratio $n_{12} = 100$. Consider the curves in Fig. 25: if the phase curves for $\bar{V}$ and $\bar{T}$ waves display the form of broken lines (in the case $n_{12} \neq 1$) and, consequently, they determine different velocities in the first and second layers (cf. the formulas for the velocities), then the curves for the phases of an intensity wave, at the same impedance ratios, will present the form of a straight line, corresponding to a constant value of the differential velocity down the layers of the medium.

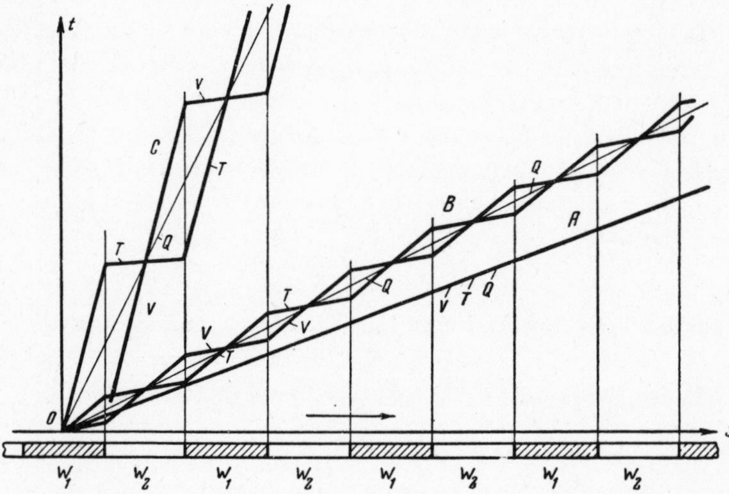

Fig. 25. Phase travel-time curves for $\bar{V}$, $\bar{T}$, and $\bar{Q}$ modes in a periodically layered medium, when $\omega \to 0$, for the three following wave impedance relations: A) $\frac{W_1}{W_2} = 1$, B) $\frac{W_1}{W_2} = 5$, and C) $\frac{W_1}{W_2} = 100$, other conditions being equal. For simplicity, it is assumed that $c_1 = c_2 = c$; $l_1 = l_2$.

2. For purposes of simulation using artificial media [22, 28, 29], consisting of lumped masses (self-induction) and elasticities (capacitances), it is of interest to investigate the microstructure of the resultant wave for the case $\omega \to 0$ in a periodically layered medium (Fig. 16) under the following critical conditions. Suppose that the first layer presents an infinitely large elasticity $K_1 \to \infty$ and a finite linear density M_1 (corresponding to a "lumped" mass); the second layer may then have a finite value of K_2 and an infinitesimally small value of $M_2 \to 0$ (corresponding in turn to a "lumped" elasticity). Under those conditions, the periodically layered medium will reflect, with sufficient accuracy, a one-dimensional "homogeneous" lattice model of an elastic medium [22].

The formulas for the differential velocities (194) for different modes and layers, under those conditions, assume the following form (taking into account the fact that $W_1 = \sqrt{K_1 M_1} \to \infty$; $W_2 = \sqrt{K_2 M_2} \to 0$; $c_1 = \sqrt{\frac{K_1}{M_1}} \to \infty$; $c_2 = \sqrt{\frac{K_2}{M_2}} \to \infty$, and neglecting terms of the second order of smallness:

$$\left.\begin{aligned}
c'_{1V} &= c_1 \sqrt{\frac{W_1 \tau_2}{W_2 \tau_1}} = \sqrt{\frac{l_2}{l_1}} \cdot \sqrt{\frac{W_1 c_1^3}{W_2 c_2}} = \sqrt{\frac{l_2}{l_1}} \cdot \sqrt[4]{\frac{K_1 M\, K_1^3 M_2}{K_2 M_2 M_1^3 K_2}} = \\
&= \sqrt{\frac{l_2}{l_1}} \cdot \sqrt[4]{\frac{K_1^4}{K_2^2 M_1^2}} \to \infty; \\
c'_{2V} &= c_2 \sqrt{\frac{W_2 \tau_2}{W_1 \tau_1}} = \sqrt{\frac{l_2}{l_1}} \cdot \sqrt{\frac{W_2}{W_1} c_1 c_2} = \\
&= \sqrt{\frac{l_2}{l_1}} \sqrt[4]{\frac{K_2 M_2}{K_1 M_1} \frac{K_1}{M_1} \frac{K_2}{M_2}} = \sqrt{\frac{l_2}{l_1}} \sqrt{\frac{K_2}{M_1}}; \\
c'_{1T} &= c_1 \sqrt{\frac{W_2 \tau_1}{W_1 \tau_2}} = \sqrt{\frac{l_1}{l_2}} \sqrt{\frac{W_2}{W_1} c_1 c_2} = \sqrt{\frac{l_1}{l_2}} \sqrt{\frac{K_2}{M_1}}; \\
c'_{2T} &= c_2 \sqrt{\frac{W_1 \tau_1}{W_2 \tau_2}} = \sqrt{\frac{l_1}{l_2}} \sqrt[4]{\frac{K_1 M_1}{K_2 M_2} \cdot \frac{K_2^3}{M_2^3} \cdot \frac{M_1}{K_1}} = \\
&= \sqrt{\frac{l_1}{l_2}} \sqrt[4]{\frac{K_2^2 M_1^2}{M_2^4}} \to \infty; \\
c'_{1Q} &= \frac{2c_1 \sqrt{W_1 W_2 W_1^2 \tau_1 \tau_2}}{W_1^2 \tau_2} = 2c_1 \sqrt{\frac{W_2 \tau_1}{W_1 \tau_2}} = 2\sqrt{\frac{l_1}{l_2}} \cdot \sqrt{\frac{K_2}{M_1}}; \\
c'_{2Q} &= \frac{2c_2 \sqrt{W_1 W_2 W_1^3 \tau_1 \tau_2}}{W_1^2 \tau_1} = 2c_2 \sqrt{\frac{W_2 \tau_2}{W_1 \tau_1}} = 2\sqrt{\frac{l_1}{l_2}} \sqrt{\frac{K_2}{M_1}}.
\end{aligned}\right\} \quad (258)$$

The integral velocity over the baseline $2l_1 + 2l_2$ for $\bar{V}$, $\bar{T}$ and $\bar{Q}$ modes is determined, for the conditions stipulated, in the following manner [cf. (255)]:

$$\begin{aligned}
c_{\text{II}V} = c_{\text{II}T} = c_{\text{II}Q} = c_{\text{I}} &= \frac{(l_1 + l_2)\sqrt{W_1 \cdot W_2}}{\sqrt{W_1^2 \cdot \tau_1 \cdot \tau_2}} = \\
&= \frac{l_1 + l_2}{\sqrt{l_1 \cdot l_2}} \sqrt{\frac{W_2}{W_1} c_1 c_2} = \frac{l_1 + l_2}{\sqrt{l_1 \cdot l_2}} \sqrt[2]{\frac{K_2}{M_1}}.
\end{aligned} \quad (259)$$

In the particular case where $l_1 = l_2 = l$, the differential and the integral velocities (258) and (259) assume the values:

$$\left.\begin{aligned}
&c'_{1V} = c'_{2T} = \infty; \quad c'_{2V} = c'_{1T} = \sqrt{\frac{K_2}{M_1}}; \\
&c'_{1Q} = c'_{1Q} = 2\sqrt{\frac{K_2}{M_1}} = c_{\text{II}V} = c_{\text{II}T} = c_{\text{II}Q}.
\end{aligned}\right\} \quad (260)$$

Equations (258), (259) and (260) determine the microstructure of the resultant wave in the model (discrete medium), when the wavelength is much larger than the length of a section $2l_1+2l_2$, while the amplitudes of each mode of waves, from point to point in the layered medium, are constant, since the attenuation constants $\alpha' = \alpha = 0$. The equations referred to retain their validity for a pulse traveling through the medium in question, when the predominant wavelength of that pulse is much greater than the length of a section $2l_1+2l_2$.

We learn from (258), (259) and (260) that all points of the first layer move in phase (monolithically), i.e., $c'_{1T} = c_{1V} = \infty$, while the pressure wave has a finite constant velocity, half that of the intensity wave in the same layer, $c'_{1Q} = 2c'_{1V}$.

The second layer, on the other hand, exhibits in-phase motion of the pressure wave ($c'_{2T} = \infty$), while the velocity wave propagates from point to point at a finite velocity, half that of the intensity mode ($c'_{2Q} = 2c'_{2V}$).

Let us note in conclusion the fact that the velocities (259) coincide in values with the velocities determined on the basis of computation of discrete mechanical (or electrical) circuits[1] (filters) at $\omega \to 0$ (e.g., cf. [22]).

3. Let us now investigate the variation of the integral wave properties in a single section $2l_1+2l_2$ of a periodically layered medium, as a function of the frequency ω, with $\tau_1 = \tau_2 = \tau$ assumed. The integral propagation constant (249) will in that case take on the following value

$$\vec{S}_{\text{II}} = i\, 2 \arcsin \left[\frac{W_1 + W_2}{2\sqrt{W_1 W_2}} \sin 2\tau\omega \right] = \alpha_{\text{II}} + i\beta_{\text{II}}, \tag{261}$$

and the cut-off frequencies ω_c, according to (251), are determined from the equation

---

[1] For the critical case of a periodically layered medium considered, where $K_1 \to \infty$; $M_2 \to 0$, we may obtain values of the differential and integral propagation constants for some arbitrary frequency ω, if we have recourse to (190) and (249), and carry out the indicated simplifications. The integral propagation constants over $2l_1 + 2l_2$ based on (249), assume values known for low-frequency mechanical (or electrical) filters [1, 22, 4].

$$\frac{W_1 + W_2}{2\sqrt{W_1 \cdot W_2}} \sin 2\tau\omega_c = 1, \tag{262}$$

or, in explicit form:

$$\omega_c = \frac{1}{2\tau} \arcsin\left(\frac{2\sqrt{W_1 W_2}}{W_1 + W_2}\right). \tag{263}$$

We introduce at this point the additional restraint $W_1 = 3W_2$. Then we determine, from (263), the following cut-off frequencies:

$$\omega_c = \frac{\pi n}{6\tau} = \frac{\pi nc}{6l}, \tag{264}$$

where $n = 1, 2, 3, \ldots$

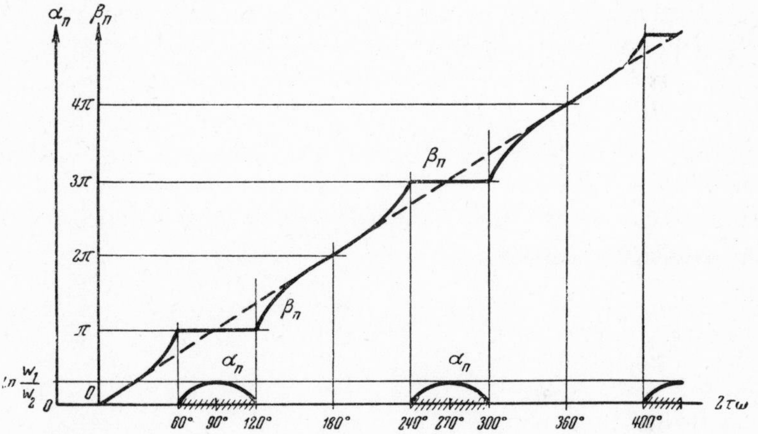

Fig. 26. Variation in the integral propagation constant for a section of a periodically layered medium as a function of the frequency ω. It is assumed that $\tau_1 = \tau_2 = \tau$ and $n_{12} = \frac{W_1}{W_2} = 3$. The hatched portions of the abscissa indicate attenuation bands.

Figure 26 presents a graph of the integral propagation constant for a section $2l_1 + 2l_2$ of a periodically layered medium, based on (261) with the assumption $n_{12} = \frac{W_1}{W_2} = 3$. The cut-off frequencies on that graph correspond to the values in (264).

From Fig. 26, we learn that when the frequency ω is increased from 0 to ∞, a periodicity asserts itself in the pass bands (transparency bands) and in the attenuation or stop bands (scattering bands) of the resultant waves traversing the layered medium.

For frequency bands where attenuation of the wave takes place, we determine the integral constant α_{II}. The integral propagation constant (261) for the attenuation band is written in the following form:

$$\vec{S}_{II} = 2 \operatorname{Arsh}\left[i \frac{W_1 + W_2}{2\sqrt{W_1 W_2}} \cdot \sin 2\tau\omega\right]. \tag{265}$$

We then take the logarithm of the inverse hyperbolic function:

$$\vec{S}_{II} = 2 \ln\left[i \frac{W_1 + W_2}{2\sqrt{W_1 W_2}} \sin 2\tau\omega + \sqrt{1 - \frac{(W_1 + W_2)^2}{4W_1 W_2} \sin^2 2\tau\omega}\right] \tag{266}$$

For the attenuation band in the layered medium, the radicand of the equation obtained is less than zero [cf. the inequality (252)], so that we remove the minus sign from under the radical sign:

$$\vec{S}_{II} = 2 \ln\left\{i\left[\frac{W_1 + W_2}{2\sqrt{W_1 W_2}} \sin 2\tau\omega + \sqrt{\frac{(W_1 + W_2)^2}{4W_1 W_2} \sin^2 2\tau\omega - 1}\right]\right\}. \tag{267}$$

Substituting $i = e^{i\frac{\pi}{2}}$, we eventually arrive at the value of the integral attenuation constant α_{II}:

$$\vec{S}_{II} = \alpha_{II} + i\beta_{II} = \ln\left[\frac{W_1 + W_2}{2\sqrt{W_1 W_2}} \cdot \sin 2\tau\omega + \right.$$

$$\left. + \sqrt{\frac{(W_1 + W_2)^2}{4W_1 W_2} \sin^2 2\tau\omega - 1}\right] + i\pi k, \tag{268}$$

where $\beta_{II} = \pi k$; $k = 1, 3, 5, \ldots$ The maximum of attenuation of waves in a section of a layered medium will take place at the frequencies determined from the equation $\sin 2\tau\omega = 1$, and is equal to α_{max}:

$$\alpha_{max} = \ln\left(\frac{W_1 + W_2}{2\sqrt{W_1 W_2}} + \sqrt{\frac{(W_1 \mp W_2)^2}{4W_1 W_2}}\right). \tag{269}$$

This leads us, after some algebra, to:

$$\alpha_{max} = \ln\left(\frac{W_1}{W_2}\right); \quad \alpha_{max} = \ln\left(\frac{W_2}{W_1}\right), \tag{270}$$

where the second value, i.e., $\alpha_{max} = \ln\left(\frac{W_2}{W_1}\right)$, has no physical significance under our assumption $n_{12} = \frac{W_1}{W_2} = 3$ (it does have significance for the resultant wave going in the opposing direction, however). The graph for the attenuation factor α_{II}, for the case under consideration, is plotted in Fig. 26.

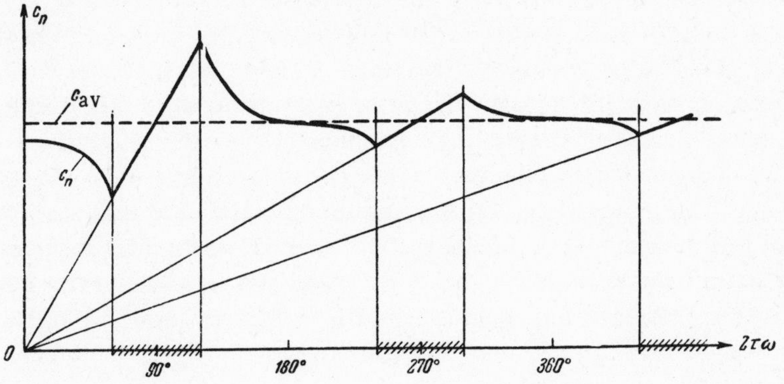

Fig. 27. Variation in the integral velocity of propagation for a section of a periodically layered medium as a function of the frequency ω. It is assumed that $\tau_1 = \tau_2 = \tau$ and $n_{12} = \frac{W_1}{W_2} = 3$; the mean velocity c_{av} is computed for a section baseline $(2l_1 + 2l_2)$ based on the formula for mean velocities in geometric seismics.

Taking as point of departure the value of the integral phase constant β_{II} for the pass band (261) and for the attenuation band (268), as well as (75), we then proceed to find the values of the integral velocities of propagation through a section of layered medium:

$$c_{\text{II}} = \frac{\omega\, 2\,(l_1 + l_2)}{\beta_{\text{II}}} = \frac{(l_1 + l_2)\,\omega}{\arcsin\left[\frac{W_1 + W_2}{2\sqrt{W_1 W_2}} \sin 2\tau\omega\right]} \tag{271a}$$

$$c_{\text{II}} = \frac{\omega_2\,(l_1 + l_2)\,2}{\pi K}, \tag{271b}$$

where $\tau_1 = \tau_2 = \tau$; $n_{12} = \frac{W_1}{W_2} = 3$. Formula (271a) is valid for the pass band, while (271b) holds for the attenuation band.

The graph plotted in Fig. 27 for the integral velocity c_n through a section of a periodically layered medium is based on (271). The horizontal dashed line indicating c_{av} on the graph represents the mean or average velocity computed on the basis of the formula for mean velocities taken from geometric seismics:

$$c_{av} = \frac{2l_1 + 2l_2}{\frac{2l_1}{c_1} + \frac{2l_2}{c_2}}. \tag{272}$$

We see readily from Fig. 27 that, at low frequencies $\omega \to 0$, the true average velocity c_{II} of harmonic waves in a periodically layered medium is less than the average velocity c_{av}, based on the formula taken from geometric seismics. Then, as ω increases, the velocity c_{II} oscillates about the value c_{av} with continually decreasing excursions; at rather high frequencies ω, the velocity c_{II} becomes a practically constant quantity, independent of ω and equal to c_{av}. This graph (Fig. 27) may be interpreted also this way: dispersion of waves in a periodically layered medium is practically absent both at rather low ($\tau\omega \to 0$) frequencies and at rather high ($\tau\omega \to \infty$) frequencies; in the middle frequency band, a periodic alternation of regions with positive and with negative dispersion is observed.

The dispersion and attenuation of the waves observed in periodically layered media correspond to Kasterin's findings [25] for similar media.

4. Let us now investigate the variation in the integral wave properties $(2l_1 + 2l_2)$ of a periodically layered medium as a function of the frequency ω for another more general case: $\tau_1 = 2\tau_2$; $n_{12} = \frac{W_1}{W_2} = 2$.

First of all, we must determine the cut-off frequencies ω_c. The equations for the cut-off frequencies (250) under our particular conditions assume the following form:

$$\left\{\begin{array}{l} \frac{W_2}{W_1} = \operatorname{tg}(\omega_c 2\tau_2)\operatorname{tg}\omega_c\tau_2 = \frac{1}{2}; \\ \frac{W_1}{W_2} = \operatorname{tg}(\omega_c 2\tau_2)\operatorname{tg}\omega_c\tau_2 = 2; \end{array}\right. \qquad \left\{\begin{array}{l} \frac{W_1}{W_2} = -\frac{\operatorname{tg}(\omega_c 2\tau_2)}{\operatorname{tg}\omega_c\tau_2} = 2; \\ \frac{W_1}{W_2} = -\frac{\operatorname{tg}\omega_c\tau_2}{\operatorname{tg}(\omega_c 2\tau_2)} = 2. \end{array}\right. \tag{273}$$

Replacing the double-angle tangents by $\operatorname{tg}\omega_c\tau_2$, and determining $\operatorname{tg}\omega_c\tau_2$, from each equation, we obtain as a result:

$$\left\{\begin{array}{l} \operatorname{tg}\omega_c\tau_2 = \pm\frac{1}{\sqrt{5}}; \\ \operatorname{tg}\omega_c\tau_2 = \pm\frac{1}{\sqrt{2}}; \end{array}\right. \qquad \left\{\begin{array}{l} \operatorname{tg}\omega_c\tau_2 = \pm\sqrt{2}; \\ \operatorname{tg}\omega_c\tau_2 = \pm\sqrt{5}. \end{array}\right. \tag{274}$$

This leads us to a determination of the cut-off frequencies ω_c (τ_2 being known):

$$\begin{cases} \omega_c\tau_2 = 24°;\ 156°;\ \ldots \\ \omega_c\tau_2 = 35°;\ 145°;\ \ldots \end{cases} \qquad \begin{cases} \omega_c\tau_2 = 55°;\ 125°;\ \ldots \\ \omega_c\tau_2 = 66°;\ 114°;\ \ldots \end{cases} \tag{275}$$

The integral propagation constant $\vec{S}_{II}$ of the section (248) assumes, in the case of the pass band, the following form (with the conditions $\tau_1 = 2\tau_2$ and $n_{12} = 2$ satisfied):

$$\vec{S}_{II} = 0 + i2\operatorname{arctg}\sqrt{\frac{(2\operatorname{tg}\omega 2\tau_2 + \operatorname{tg}\omega\tau_2)(2\operatorname{tg}\omega\tau_2 + \operatorname{tg}\omega 2\tau_2)}{(2 - \operatorname{tg}\omega\tau_2 \cdot \operatorname{tg}\omega_2\tau_2)(1 - 2\operatorname{tg}\omega\tau_2 \cdot \operatorname{tg}\omega_2\tau_2)}} = \alpha_{II} + i\beta_{II}. \tag{276}$$

For frequency bands where attenuation of the waves takes place in the section (and, consequently, in the layered medium as a whole), the integral propagation constant $\vec{S}_{II}$ (248), as shown, has a negative radicand. In that case, we introduce i beneath the radical sign in (248) and as a result obtain the following value of $\vec{S}_{II}$ for the attenuation band:

$$\vec{S}_{II} = 2\operatorname{Arth}\sqrt{\frac{(W_1\operatorname{tg}\omega\tau_1 + W_2\operatorname{tg}\omega\tau_2)(W_1\operatorname{tg}\omega\tau_2 + W_2\operatorname{tg}\omega\tau_1)}{(W_1 - W_2\operatorname{tg}\omega\tau_1 \cdot \operatorname{tg}\omega\tau_2)(W_1\operatorname{tg}\omega\tau_1\operatorname{tg}\omega\tau_2 - W_2)}} + $$
$$+ i\pi k = \alpha_{II} + i\beta_{II}, \tag{277}$$

where $k = 1, 2, 3, \ldots$ For the particular case in point and for $n_{12} = 2$, the integral attenuation constant which we found assumes the following form:

$$\alpha_{II} = 2\operatorname{Arth}\sqrt{\frac{(2\operatorname{tg}\omega 2\tau_2 + \operatorname{tg}\omega\tau_2)(2\operatorname{gt}\omega\tau_2 + \operatorname{tg}\omega 2\tau_2}{(2 - \operatorname{tg}\omega 2\tau_2 \cdot \operatorname{tg}\omega\tau_2)(2\operatorname{tg}\omega 2\tau_2\operatorname{tg}\omega\tau_2 - 1)}}. \tag{278}$$

Finally, the integral velocity of propagation c_{II} for all modes of waves traversing the section of the layered medium is determined in accord with β_{II} in (276), (277) and (75):

$$\left.\begin{aligned} c_{II} &= \frac{\omega(l_1 + l_2)}{\operatorname{arctg}\sqrt{\dfrac{(2\operatorname{tg}\omega 2\tau_2 + \operatorname{tg}\omega\tau_2)(2\operatorname{tg}\omega\tau_2 + \operatorname{tg}\omega_2\tau_2)}{(2 - \operatorname{tg}\omega\tau_2 \cdot \operatorname{tg}\omega 2\tau_2)(1 - 2\operatorname{tg}\omega\tau_2 \cdot \operatorname{tg}\omega 2\tau_2)}}}; \\ c_{II} &= \frac{\omega 2(l_1 + l_2)}{\pi k}, \end{aligned}\right\} \tag{279}$$

where $k = 1, 2, 3, \ldots$ The last equation determines the velocity through a section for the frequency band ω, where attenuation of the waves takes place.

The graph plotted in Fig. 28 for the integral velocity c_{II} over the baseline $2l_1 + 2l_2$, as a function of the frequency ω, is based on (279).

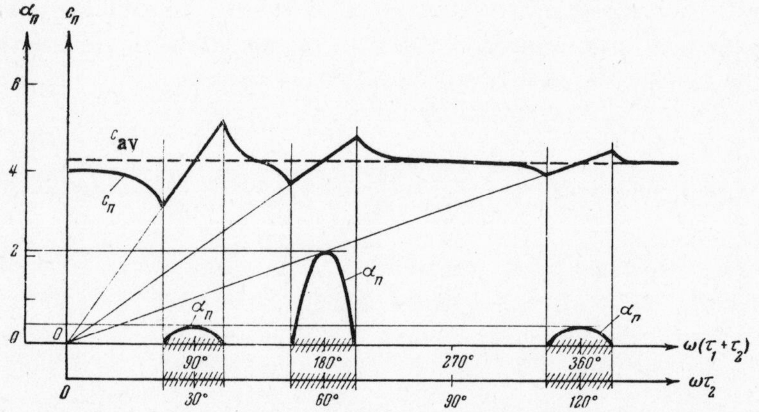

Fig. 28. Variation in the integral velocity of propagation c_{Π} and of the attenuation constant α_{Π} for a section $(2l_1 + 2l_2)$ of a periodically layered medium, as a function of frequency ω. It is assumed that $\tau_1 = 2\tau_2$ and $n_{12} = \frac{W_1}{W_2} = 2$. The mean velocity c_{av} is computed for a section baseline on the basis of the formula for mean velocities taken from geometric seismics. The hatched portions of the abscissa indicate attenuation bands.

For the attenuation bands (hatched abscissa), a graph of the integral attenuation factor α_{II} is given. The mean velocity c_{av} over the baseline $2l_1 + 2l_2$, computed on the basis of the formula for the mean velocities borrowed from geometric seismics, is shown on the graph by the straight line c_{av}.

We readily learn, from the graphs (Fig. 27 and 28), that in the case of steady-state oscillations, with the frequency increasing from 0 to ∞, the layered medium (Fig. 16) periodically changes in state: it transmits the elastic wave with complete freedom (pass band), then becomes a medium exhibiting attenuation (attenuation band). The attenuation bands are related to the inherent oscillations of a periodically layered medium, reminiscent in some of their traits to standing waves, mainly because there exist points $u = 0$ and $y = 0$ (cf. Fig. 21), for even and odd layers in the medium, in which the differential velocities vanish (the nodes of the velocity, pressure, or intensity waves).

Periodically Layered Media Having n Homogeneous Layers Accommodated Within a Period of Structure L.

In conclusion, we shall briefly point to the possibility of solving the wave problems for infinite periodically layered media having, within a period, an arbitrary number of layers. An example of one such medium may be seen in Fig. 29. A comparison of the solution

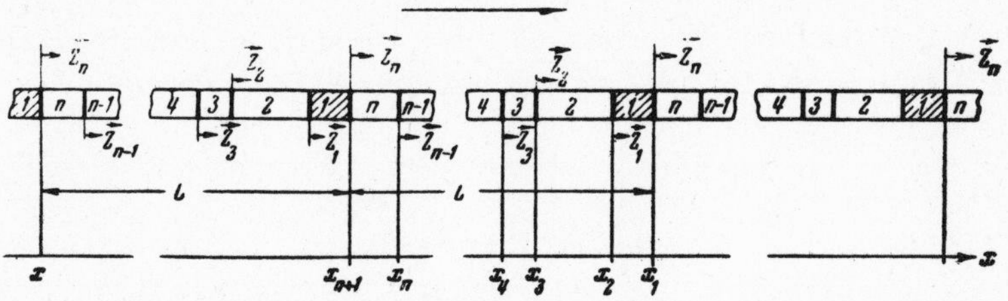

Fig. 29. Infinite periodically layered medium having n homogeneous layers in a period of structure (in a section) L. $\bar{W}_k$, $\bar{q}_{0k}$, and l_k are, respectively, the wave impedance, the propagation constant, and the length of the layer, were k assumes values ranging from 1 to n.

in that case, using the method of four-pole networks described above, presents no basic difficulties. However, the investigation of the micro- and macrostructure of the waves involves highly cumbersome equations and transformations. In connection with those difficulties, we may indicate at this point only a general approach to the solution of similar problems. We must first of all determine the values of the input impedances of a periodically layered medium (cf. Fig. 29) for the instantaneous coordinate x. Layered media exhibiting a periodic structure with a period length L are characterized by the fact that (cf. iterative impedances, e.g., in [2]) the input impedances in a single direction toward the terminations of the baseline L are equal for an arbitrary placing of L relative to the layers of the medium. Let us place L such as indicated in Fig. 29. The portion of the periodically layered medium of length L will be termed a section, whereupon the entire infinite medium may be represented as composed of an infinite number of identical sections, series-connected. Let us make the calculations for one section of the periodically layered medium, assuming the parameters of the discrete layers of the section to be known: $\bar{W}_k$ being the wave impedance, $\bar{q}_{0k}$ the propagation constant of a homogeneous layer, and l_k the thickness of the layer where k assumes any value ranging over 1, 2, 3, . . . on up to n. Parameters $\bar{W}_k$ and $\bar{q}_{02}$ are given in operational notation, and also take into account, in the general case, resistive losses in the layers; the definitive solution to the problem is then obtained as a function of the Heaviside operator p, which yields the fundamental possibility of studying the transient mode of oscillations in the given medium exhibiting absorption.

The input impedances of the section in layers 1, 2, 3, . . ., n are determined on the basis of the method described in section 2 of this article. In sum, we have a system of n equations:

$$\left.\begin{array}{l}
\vec{Z}_{1(x)} = \bar{W}_1 \dfrac{\vec{Z}_n + \bar{W}_1 \operatorname{th} \bar{q}_{01}(x_1 - x)}{\vec{Z}_n \operatorname{th} \bar{q}_{01}(x_1 - x) + \bar{W}_1} \Bigg|_{x_1 \geqslant x \geqslant x_2} = f_1(x, p), \\
\vec{Z}_{2(x)} = \bar{W}_2 \dfrac{\vec{Z}_1 + \bar{W}_2 \operatorname{th} \bar{q}_{02}(x_2 - x)}{\vec{Z}_1 \operatorname{th} \bar{q}_{02}(x_2 - x) + \bar{W}_2} \Bigg|_{x_2 \geqslant x \geqslant x_3} = f_2(x, p), \\
\vec{Z}_3(x) = \bar{W}_3 \dfrac{\vec{Z}_2 + \bar{W}_3 \operatorname{th} \bar{q}_{03}(x_3 - x)}{\vec{Z}_2 \operatorname{th} \bar{q}_{03}(x_3 - x) + \bar{W}_3} \Bigg|_{x_3 \geqslant x \geqslant x_4} = f_3(x, p), \\
\cdots\cdots\cdots\cdots\cdots\cdots \\
\cdots\cdots\cdots\cdots\cdots\cdots \\
\cdots\cdots\cdots\cdots\cdots\cdots \\
\vec{Z}_n(x) = \bar{W}_n \dfrac{\vec{Z}_{n-1} + \bar{W}_n \operatorname{th} \bar{q}_{0n}(x_n - x)}{\vec{Z}_{n-1} \cdot \operatorname{th} \bar{q}_{0n}(x_n - x) + \bar{W}_n} \Bigg|_{x_n \geqslant x \geqslant x_{n+1}} = f_n(x, p),
\end{array}\right\} \quad (280)$$

where $\vec{Z}_1$; $\vec{Z}_2$; $\vec{Z}_3$ . . . $\vec{Z}_n$ are the input impedances at the interfaces between layers (cf. Fig. 29); $\vec{Z}_1(x)$; $\vec{Z}_2(x)$; $\vec{Z}_3(x)$ . . . $\vec{Z}_n(x)$ are the input impedances for the instantaneous coordinate x, which varies over the range indicated for each equation.

The determination of the input impedances for the instantaneous coordinate x from x_1 to x_{n+1}, i.e., for the period of structure L, is related, as is apparent from the equations obtained (280), to a knowledge of the input impedances at the interfaces of the layered medium. That is why we equate x, in (280), for each equation, to the limit on the right, then obtaining a system of n equations in n unknown input impedances at the interfaces between layers. By solving this system, which leads to quadratic equations, we obtain all of the values of the input impedances at the interfaces: $\vec{Z}_1$; $\vec{Z}_2$; $\vec{Z}_3$ . . . $\vec{Z}_n$. By substituting the values obtained for the input impedances at the interfaces into our system of equations (280), we at the same time find the unknown input impedances for the section of the periodically layered medium, for the instantaneous coordinate x as a function of the Heaviside operator p.

The differential propagation constants of the $\bar{V}$ and $\bar{T}$ modes for each homogeneous layer are then determined [according to (16), (25), in addition to using the input impedances found (280)] in the following form:

$$\left.\begin{aligned} &\vec{D}_{1V}=\frac{\vec{Z}_1(x)}{\overline{W}_1}\bar{q}_{01};\quad \vec{D}_{2V}=\frac{\vec{Z}_2(x)}{\overline{W}_2}\bar{q}_{02};\quad \vec{D}_{3V}=\frac{\vec{Z}_3(x)}{\overline{W}_3}\bar{q}_{03};\quad \ldots;\\ &\qquad\qquad\qquad\qquad\qquad\qquad\vec{D}_{nV}=\frac{\vec{Z}_n(x)}{\overline{W}_n}\bar{q}_{0n};\\ &\vec{D}_{1T}=\frac{\overline{W}_1}{\vec{Z}_1(x)}\bar{q}_{01};\quad \vec{D}_{2T}=\frac{\overline{W}_2}{\vec{Z}_2(x)}\bar{q}_{02};\quad \vec{D}_{3T}=\frac{\overline{W}_3}{\vec{Z}_3(x)}\bar{q}_{03};\quad \ldots;\\ &\qquad\qquad\qquad\qquad\qquad\qquad\vec{D}_{nT}=\frac{W_n}{\vec{Z}_n(x)}\bar{q}_{0n}. \end{aligned}\right\} \quad (281)$$

These equations are dependent on the Heaviside operator p and on the coordinate x, and determine the microstructure of the waves traversing a periodically layered medium (Fig. 29).

The integral propagation constants for $\bar{V}$ and $\bar{T}$ modes, i.e., $\vec{S}_V$ and $\vec{S}_T$, are found by conventional integration with respect to x over the values obtained for $\vec{D}_V$ and $\vec{D}_T$, i.e., the quantities in (281), which yields the possibility of studying the external wave properties (the macrostructure of the waves) traversing periodically layered media. According to section 1, $\vec{S}_{\text{II}V}$ and $\vec{S}_{\text{II}T}$ for a single section of length L will be:

$$\left.\begin{aligned} &\vec{S}_{\text{II}V}=\int\limits_{x_{n+1}}^{x_n}\vec{D}_{nV}dx+\int\limits_{x_n}^{x_{n-1}}\vec{D}_{(n-1)V}\,dx+\int\limits_{x_{n-1}}^{x_{n-2}}\vec{D}_{(n-2)V}dx+\ldots+\\ &\qquad\qquad\qquad+\int\limits_{x_3}^{x_2}\vec{D}_{2V}dx+\int\limits_{x_2}^{x_1}\vec{D}_{1V}dx=F_V(p),\\ &\vec{S}_{\text{II}T}=\int\limits_{x_{n+1}}^{x_n}\vec{D}_{nT}dx+\int\limits_{x_n}^{x_{n-1}}\vec{D}_{(n-1)T}\,dx+\int\limits_{x_{n-1}}^{x_{n-2}}\vec{D}_{(n-2)T}dx+\ldots+\\ &\qquad\qquad\qquad+\int\limits_{x_3}^{x_2}\vec{D}_{2T}dx=\int\limits_{x_2}^{x_1}\vec{D}_{1T}dx=F_T(p). \end{aligned}\right\} \quad (282)$$

It may then be shown, in similar fashion, as this is done for a doubly layered periodic medium, that $\vec{S}_{\text{II}V}=\vec{S}_{\text{II}T}$.

The external wave properties of the sum of the sections are found by summing over the values of $\vec{S}_{\text{II}}$. Thus, in the case of k sections, we get:

$$\vec{S}_k = k \cdot \vec{S}_{\text{II}V} = k \cdot \vec{S}_{\text{II}T} = F(k_1 p),$$

where k acquires the sense of a coordinate assuming the values of a discrete series of numbers 1, 2, 3, . . . ∞.

CONCLUSIONS

We have discussed the micro- and macrostructure of waves traversing nonhomogeneous media. A general conclusion which follows from the research undertaken on the microstructure of the resultant waves reduces to the following.

For nonhomogeneous media, the velocity waves $\bar{V}$ and pressure waves $\bar{T}$ in the resultant wave proceed everywhere in opposite directions: when the differential velocity of propagation c' of one wave increases beyond the value of the computed velocity c of the portion of the medium in question, the velocity c' of the other wave decreases (and conversely), whereupon the amplitude of the respective waves at points considered in the medium increase or decrease, in similar fashion to the velocities c'.

The velocity of an intensity wave c'_Q everywhere assumes the mean value lying between c'_V and c'_T, whereby c'_Q may be larger or smaller than the velocity c of a homogeneous wave in the portion of the medium under consideration. However, the velocity c'_Q of an intensity wave near interfaces in the medium (from the side on which the wave impinges) is everywhere less than the computed velocity c, independently of the wave impedance ratio of the adjoining layers (with the exception of the case where the wave impedances are equal). This conclusion is essential for understanding the laws governing the propagation of elastic impulses through periodically layered media and other media, when the dominant wavelength is much greater than the inhomogeneity of the medium. In this connection, for example, it is natural to expect a lowering of the value of the velocity in media with continuously varying elastic characteristics, since similar media may be represented by a series of infinitesimally small homogeneous sections with a corresponding distribution of wave impedances and velocities of propagation c.

From a consideration of the wave problems presented, we see that the determination of the velocity of propagation and of the amplitudes of sinusoidal waves in fine-scale nonhomogeneous media constitutes a laborious problem, particularly in media having continuously varying elastic characteristics. The difficulties are appreciably magnified when it is required to investigate the propagation of a wave impulse through a nonhomogeneous medium. The simulation of wave phenomena, e.g., on electrical models [28, 30] is therefore of particular interest, even for this comparatively narrow range of seismic wave problems.

SUMMARY

The paper, with the aid of the theory of electrical four-pole transmission lines, treats the general method of the solution of a whole class of one-dimensional wave problems for nonhomogeneous continuous media, including wave problems relating to media with continuously varying elastic characteristics. The author introduces the concept of the differential propagation constant, with the aid of which the wave problems are solved, and, on the other hand, the microstructure of the waves in nonhomogeneous media is studied. The solutions to the wave problems are presented in operational form, making it possible to study the transient behavior of oscillations in nonhomogeneous media by the techniques of operational calculus.

A detailed investigation of the micro- and macrostructure of sinusoidal waves is carried out for a number of nonhomogeneous media: 1) with a single interface, 2) with two interfaces, 3) with periodically repeating layers.

As a result of the consideration of the microstructure of the resultant waves, the laws governing the variation of the differential velocity (phase velocity of propagation of a wave, measured over an infinitesimally small baseline) are determined, as a function of the wave impedance ratio at interfaces, the coordinate x of the one-dimensional nonhomogeneous medium, and the frequency ω. The amplitude variations in the resultant wave are subjected to study at the same time. The investigation extends to a consideration of velocity waves $\bar{V}$, pressure waves $\bar{T}$, and intensity waves $\bar{Q}$ in nonhomogeneous media.

As a result of the study of the macrostructure of the waves in nonhomogeneous media, the frequency dependencies of the phase velocities, measured over a finite baseline (dispersion curves) are obtained, in the case of a single interface, two interfaces, and a periodically repeating structure of layers.

The paper subjects to detailed investigation periodically layered media, having two layers accommodated within a period of the structure. The equations obtained for the cut-off frequencies make it possible to determine the cut-off frequencies that define the limits of the pass (transparency) band and attenuation band in the medium in question.

For frequencies $\omega \to 0$, the (integral) velocities for the $\bar{V}$, $\bar{T}$, and $\bar{Q}$ modes in discrete layers are determined, as well as in a whole section or over some arbitrary baseline of a periodically layered medium.

Graphs are constructed for the (integral) velocity of propagation for a section of a periodically layered medium, as a frequency function (dispersion curves), and are compared with the value of the velocity computed on the basis of the formula for mean velocities borrowed from geometric seismics and, in connection with that and with previous findings, the limits of applicability of geometric seismics in the treatment of one-dimensional nonhomogeneous media are considered.

At the end of the paper, the solution of the wave problem in periodically layered media having an arbitrary number of layers within a period of the structure is considered briefly.

Finally, the solutions obtained for continuous media may be applied to the design of discrete (lattice) models. This requires replacing the wave impedances $\bar{W}$ and the propagation constants $\bar{q}_0$ of continuous layers of the media by the corresponding known values of the wave impedances and of the propagation constants of discrete "homogeneous layers" of the model.

LITERATURE CITED

1. A.A. Kharkevich, Teoriya Elektroakusticheskikh Apparatov [Theory of Electroacoustical Equipment] M[oskva], Svyaz'izdat, 1940.
2. P.K. Akul'shin, I.A. Kosheev and K.E. Kul'batskii, Teoriya Svyazi po Provadom [The Theory of Wire Communications] M[oskva], Svyaz'izdat, 1940.
3. B.P. Aseev, Kolebatel'nye Tsepi [Oscillatory Circuits] M[oskva], Svyaz'izdat, 1938.
4. T.E. Shea, Chetyrekhpolyusniki i Elektricheskie Fil'try, M[oskva], Svyaz'izdat, 1934 [Transmission Networks and Wave Filters, D. Van Nostrand Co., 1929].
5. A.I. Belov, "Sostavlenie elektricheskikh skhem, ekvivalentnykh mekhanicheskim kolebatel'nym sistemam" [Comparison of electrical circuits equivalent to mechanical oscillatory systems]. Z[hurnal] T[ekhnicheskoi] F[iziki] [Journal of Technical Physics] 5, 9 (1935).
6. G.A. Gamburtsev, Seismicheskie Metody Razvedki [Seismic Methods in Prospecting] Part 1. M[oskva]-L[eningrad], ONTI, 1937.
7. G.A. Gamburtsev, "O sushchestvovanii elektro-mekhanicheskikh analogii" [On the existence of electromechanical analogies] Dokl[ady] AN SSSR [Proceedings of The Academy of Sciences of the USSR] 60, 8, 1950.
8. B.N. Ivakin, Modelirovanie Mikro- i Makrostruktury Voln v Neodnorodnykh Sredakh. Dissertatsiya [Simulation of the Micro- and Macrostructure of Waves in Nonhomogeneous Media. Doctorate Thesis] M[oskva], Geofiz. Institut AN SSSR, 1952.
9. G.S. Gorelik, Kolebaniya i Volny [Oscillations and Waves] M[oskva]-L[eningrad], Gostekhizdat, 1950.

10. S.E. Khaikin, Mekhanika [Mechanics], M[oskva]-L[eningrad], Gostekhizdat, 1947.
11. V.V. Furduev, Elektroakustika [Electroacoustics] M[oskva]-L[eningrad], Gostekhizdat, 1948.
12. P.M. Morse, Kolebaniya i Zvuk, M[oskva]-L[eningrad], Gostekhizdat, 1949 [Vibration and Sound, McGraw-Hill Book Co., Inc., N.Y., 1948].
13. A.H. Davis, Sovremennaya Akustika, M[oskva]-L[eningrad], GONTI, 1938 [Modern Acoustics, Macmillan, London, 1934].
14. I.P. Kosminskaya, Interferentsiya Seismicheskikh Voln, Vyzvannykh Garmonicheskimi i Impul'snymi Istochnikami. Dissertatsiya [Interference in Seismic Waves Due to Harmonic and Pulsed Sources. Doctorate Thesis] M[oskva], Geofiz. Institut AN SSSR, 1951.
15. G.A. Gamburtsev, Seismicheskie Metody Razvedki, [Seismic Methods in Prospecting] Part II. M[oskva]-L[eningrad], ONTI, 1938.
16. Yu.V. Riznichenko, "Geometricheskaya seismika sloistykh sred" [Geometric Seismics of Layered Media], Trudy I[nst.] T[eoret.] G[eofiz.] AN SSSR [Proceedings of the Institute of Theoretical Geophysics of the Academy of Sciences of the USSR] 2, 1, 1946.
17. V.L. Ginzburg, Teoriya Rasprostraneniya Radiovoln v Ionosfere [Theory of the Propagation of Radio Waves in the Ionosphere] M[oskva]-L[eningrad], Gostekhizdat, 1949.
18. L. Eckart, "Die Reaktanz-und Vierpoltheorie inhomogener idealer Leitungen," Hochfrequenztechnik und Elektroakustik, 55, 6, 1940.
19. D.V. Rayleigh, Teoriya Zvuka, T[om] I i II, M[oskva]-L[eningrad], Gostekhizdat, 1955 [Theory of Sound, Vols. I and II, Dover, N.Y., 1945].
20. V.V. Stepanov, Kurs Differentsial'nykh Uravnenii [A Course in Differential Equations], M[oskva]-L[eningrad], Gostekhizdat, 1945.
21. D.N. Watson, Teoriya Besselevykh Funktsii, Ch[ast'] I, M[oskva], IL, 1949 [Theory of Bessel Functions, Part I, Cambridge-New York, 1922].
22. B.N. Ivakin, "Uprugie volny v odnomernykh i dvumernykh setochnykh modelyakh nepreryvnykh sred," [Elastic waves in one-dimensional and two-dimensional lattice models of con-

tinuous media], Trudy Geofiz. Inst. AN SSSR [Proceedings of the Geophysical Institute of the Academy of Sciences of the USSR], 9 (136), 84, 1950.

23. I.N. Bronshtein and K.A. Semendyaev, Spravochnik po Matematike [Manual on Mathematics], M[oskva]-L[eningrad], Gostekhizdat, 1945.

24. B.D. Tartakovskii, "O perekhode zvukovykh voln cherez granitsy tverdykh i zhidkikh sred" [On the traversal of a solid-liquid interface by sound waves], Z[hur.] T[ekhn.] F[iz.] [Journal of Technical Physics], 21, 10, 1951.

25. I.P. Kasterin, O Rasprostranenii Voln v Neodnorodnoi Srede [On Wave Propagation in a Nonhomogeneous Medium] Part I. M[oskva], 1903.

26. R.B. Lindsay, "The filtration of sound, II," J. Appl. Phys. 10, 680, 1939.

27. Yu.V. Riznichenko, "O seismicheskoi kvazianizotropii" [On seismic quasi-anisotropy], Izvestiya AN SSSR, seriya geofiz.-geograf. [Bulletin of the Academy of Sciences of the USSR, geophysical and geographical series] 13, 6, 1949.

28. L.I. Gutenmakhen, Elektricheskie Modeli [Electrical Models] M[oskva]-L[eningrad], Izd.-vo AN SSSR, 1949.

29. P.E. Krasnushkin, "Normal'nye volny v tsepochechnykh mnogopolyusnykh fil'trakh" [Normal waves in sectioned multiple filters], Z[hur.] T[ekhn.] F[iz.] [Journal of Technical Physics] 17, 705, 1947.

30. Yu.V. Riznichenko, B.N. Ivakin and V.R. Bugrev, "Impul'snyi ul'trazvukovoi seismoskop" [A pulsed ultrasonic seismoscope], Izvest. AN SSSR, seriya geofiz. [Bulletin of the Academy of Sciences of the USSR, geophysical series] I, 1953.